LEARNING, ENVIRONMENT AND SUSTAINABLE DEVELOPMENT

This book is an introduction to the long history of human learning, the environment and sustainable development – about our struggles with the natural world: first for survival, then for dominance, currently for self-preservation, and in future perhaps, even for long-term, mutually beneficial co-existence. It charts the long arc of human–environment relationships through the specific lens of human learning, putting on record many of the people, ideas and events that have contributed, often unwittingly, to the global movement for sustainable development.

Human learning has always had a focus on the environment. It's something we've been engaged in ever since we began interacting with our surroundings and thinking about the impacts, outcomes and consequences of our actions and inter-actions. This unique story told by the authors is episodic rather than a connected, linear account; it probes, questions and re-examines familiar issues from novel perspectives, and looks ahead. The book is of particular interest to those studying (and teaching) courses with a focus on socio-economic and environmental sus-tainability, and non-governmental organisations whose work brings them face-to-face with the general public and social enterprises.

William Scott is Emeritus Professor of Education at the University of Bath, UK, and is Chair of Trustees of the UK's National Association for Environmental Education. He was one of the founding editors of the Routledge journal, *Environmental Education Research*.

Paul Vare is Research Convener for the School of Education at the University of Gloucestershire, UK. He has worked internationally in the voluntary sector, with large corporations and national governments, and the United Nations Economic Commission for Europe (UNECE) on education for sustainable development.

LEARNING, ENVIRONMENT AND SUSTAINABLE DEVELOPMENT

A History of Ideas

William Scott and Paul Vare

Routledge
Taylor & Francis Group

LONDON AND NEW YORK

First published 2021
by Routledge
2 Park Square, Milton Park, Abingdon, Oxon OX14 4RN

and by Routledge
52 Vanderbilt Avenue, New York, NY 10017

Routledge is an imprint of the Taylor & Francis Group, an informa business

British Library Cataloguing in Publication Data
A catalogue record for this book is available from the British Library

Library of Congress Cataloging-in-Publication Data
A catalog record has been requested for this book

ISBN: 978-0-367-22192-8 (hbk)
ISBN: 978-0-367-22193-5 (pbk)
ISBN: 978-0-429-27370-4 (ebk)

Typeset in Bembo
by Taylor & Francis Books

This book is dedicated to Jean and to Emma

CONTENTS

ILLUSTRATIONS

Figure

Table

ABBREVIATIONS

ADHD	attention deficit hyperactivity disorder
AI	artificial intelligence
ARC	Alliance of Religions and Conservation
BBC	British Broadcasting Corporation
BCE	Before Common Era
BEE	*Bulletin of Environmental Education*
CAT	Centre for Alternative Technology
CE	Common Era
CEE	Council for Environmental Education
CLOtC	Council for Learning Outside the Classroom
C&NN	Children & Nature Network
CO_2	carbon dioxide
COVID-19	Coronavirus disease 2019
CSCT	Curriculum, Sustainable development, Competences, Teacher training
DART	Double Asteroid Redirection Test
DDT	dichloro-diphenyl-trichloroethane
DeSeCo	Definition and Selection of Competencies Project
EE	environmental education
EER	*Environmental Education Research*
EFA	Education for All
ENSI	Environment and School Initiatives
EPA	US Environmental Protection Agency
ESD	education for sustainable development
FSA	Forest School Association
GDP	gross domestic product

GEEP	Global Environmental Education Partnership
GHDI	German History in Documents and Images
GSSP	Global Boundary Stratotype Section and Point
HEFCE	Higher Education Funding Council for England
HMI	Her Majesty's Inspectorate of Schools
IEEP	International Environmental Education Programme
INDC	Intended Nationally Determined Contributions
IUCN	International Union for Conservation of Nature
JEE	*Journal of Environmental Education*
MDGs	Millennium Development Goals
NAAEE	North American Association for Environmental Education
NAEE	National Association for Environmental Education (UK)
NASA	National Aeronautics and Space Administration (USA)
NGO	non-governmental organisation
NGRIP	North Greenland Ice Core Project
NSDAP	The National Socialist German Workers' Party, commonly known as the Nazi Party
NVQ	National Vocational Qualification
OEA	Outdoor Education Association
OECD	Organisation for Economic Co-operation and Development
PERE	person-environment relationship education
PERF	person-environment relationship foundations
PISA	Programme for International Student Assessment
POP	persistent organic pollutant
ppm	parts per million
PSHE	Personal, Social and Health Education
PSI	Policy Studies Institute
RE	Religious Education
RSP	A Rounder Sense of Purpose
SDEP	Sustainable Development Education Panel
SDGs	Sustainable Development Goals
SLE	significant life experience
TCPA	Town & Country Planning Association
TED	Technology, Entertainment and Design
UK	United Kingdom
UN	United Nations
UNDESD	United Nations Decade of Education for Sustainable Development
UNDP	United Nations Development Programme
UNECE	United Nations Economic Commission for Europe
UNEP	United Nations Environment Programme
UNESCO	United Nations Educational, Scientific and Cultural Organization
USA	United States of America
WCED	World Commission on Environment and Development

WCS	World Conservation Strategy
WHO	World Health Organization
WRI	World Resources Institute
WWF	World Wide Fund for Nature
XR	Extinction Rebellion

FOREWORD

There are many reasons why you might have picked up this book and glanced at this Foreword. It might simply be that your particular interest lies in sustainable development, or in learning, or in the environment. It's also possible that you combine these through a concern with environmental education, education for sustainable development, transformational education or something similar. If so, it is quite likely that you have previously come across the work of Bill Scott and Paul Vare. Scott has been a researcher with an internationally leading reputation for three decades and is also an outstanding practical educator. Vare has unsurpassed and quite extraordinarily varied experience as an environmental education practitioner, as well as being accomplished in academic research.

However, and paradoxical as it may seem, the issues that this book illuminates are at once so urgent, and so enduring, that you may have come to the volume knowing nothing of the above at all, but through other concerns. These might be quite specific: Is it possible to reduce global carbon emissions, save endangered species or change consumption patterns through education? If so, how? Can an educational focus on our environment promote learners' agency? Might such a focus improve mental health, or be a path to spiritual contentment? Underlying such questions are others, more difficult to pin down: What is the difference between *nature* and the *environment*? Is a teacher's primary responsibility to the present needs of the individual student, or to longer-term aspirations for society as a whole? Is education, itself, unnatural? Should we be seeking answers to our problems through natural-scientific research, social-scientific reimagining, or spiritual reconnection? Depending on the answers we give, what should we teach, to whom should we teach it, and how will we know when it's working?

There are many other possible questions, but at the heart of this book is a recognition that most have been asked already and – for better or worse – answered. Martin Luther King Jr. said: "We are not makers of history. We are

made by history." Then he got on with doing something about it. Our own circumstances may be unique in some ways, but if we want to do something about
where our history has landed us, then we spurn the knowledge and experience of
our predecessors at our peril.

No such spurning happens here. The book's opening section, titled *Past historic*,
recognises the value of insights from the past that, today, might be dismissed as
unscientific; but scientific language either did not then exist, or was in its absolute
infancy. Beyond the veil of contemporary standards and expectations lies something that deserves to be heard. Here you will find the source of deeply held sup-
positions that continue to be both widespread and influential. For example, the
idea that there was an original state of perfection that humans have defiled through
intensive farming, industry, war, depravity or simply eating a sacred apple, and that
this requires some form of atonement in the present, continues to shape some
policy proposals, though "state of perfection" seems a profoundly euphemistic
description of Neolithic agriculture or hunter-gatherer lifestyles. Here you will also
find the provenance of the rather more recent notion that human history might
lead eventually to some wonderful possible destination: a future state of affairs in
which everything will be fine and nothing will need to change. You will also find
evidence that things do change, whether they "need to" or not. My own favourite
insight comes in the chapter on the Greenland Norse, who were eradicated by
climate change. They had no idea what climate change was. We know exactly
what it is, though the jury is out on whether, in the end, that means we are going
to do any better than they did. They made up stories to explain what was happening. So do we. As Scott and Vare remark in the final chapter, "it will be the
stories that we choose to tell ourselves, with education having a central role in
conveying these, that may yet determine our survival".

The second section of the book, *Present imperfect*, presents an overview of the co-
development of environmental, educational, philosophical and institutional
thought and action since our environmental problem was first perceived as being
acute. Some may be surprised to discover how long ago that was. The problems
haven't been solved, but many clever and energetic people have given it their best
shot, which should at least tell us that what we should do isn't simple and obvious.
This is true not least because all interventions have unintended consequences, and
so one problem may often transform itself into another. We should also note that
while academic research, curriculum design and environmental policy development
are certainly driven by high ideals and humane concern, they are also part of the
daily drama of human life. Status and promotion may depend upon the extent to
which particular points of view are adopted, published, quoted or upheld. Changing one's mind can be professionally difficult. In the past this often fuelled
unhelpful hostility between proponents of different views. Today, by contrast, one
might sometimes think that almost any position is acceptable if it makes sense
within its own "paradigm". There is danger in that too. As education policy expert
and subsequent US Assistant Secretary of State Walter Kotschnig pointed out in
1939: "Let us keep our minds open, by all means, as long as that means keeping

our sense of perspective and seeking an understanding of the forces which mould the world. But don't keep your minds so open that your brains fall out! There are still things in this world which are true and things which are false; acts which are right and acts which are wrong."[1]

This book will challenge your brain while keeping it securely in place. It is, above all, properly educational. Scott and Vare recognise that the way forward is likely to involve simultaneously adapting to our environment, and adapting that environment to our needs. We change the environment by making a living in it and from it, but in ways that are always to some extent a surprise. That's how history got us to where we are. When you have read this book you will be better placed to do something about it.

Steve Gough
Professor Emeritus
University of Bath, UK
March 2020

Note

1 Professor Tells Students to Open Minds to Truth. *Blytheville Courier News* (Arkansas), January 27, 1940.

ACKNOWLEDGEMENTS

In writing this book we have drawn on two professional lifetimes' worth of collaborations and conversations which are too wide-ranging to list, and we owe a debt of gratitude to so many people. You know who you are. We are particularly grateful, however, for the specific advice and help of the following colleagues:

Bill Finnegan [Tamarack Media]
Charlotte Clark [Duke University]
Inka Bormann [Freie University of Berlin]
Judy Braus [North American Association for Environmental Education]
Marco Rieckmann [Vechta University]
Martha Monroe [University of Florida]
Nelleke Bak [University of Cape Town]
Nick Jones [World Heritage Trails]
Nicole Ardoin [Stanford University]
Richard Jurin [University of Northern Colorado]
Steve Martin [University of the West of England]
Tom Marcinkowski [Florida Institute of Technology]

INTRODUCTION

This book is an introduction to the long history of our learning about human–environment relationships; that is, our struggles with and within the natural world – first for survival, then for dominance, currently for self-preservation, and in future perhaps, even for long-term, mutually beneficial co-existence. We set out to (i) chart these relationships through the specific lens of human learning, putting on record many of the people, ideas and events that have contributed, often unwittingly, to the modern global movement for sustainable development; (ii) locate current efforts to achieve sustainable development within the broad history of ideas; and (iii) outline some probable and some possible future directions for sustainable development.

Our human history is clearly one of learning and the arc of this book begins with the early human experience of learning to survive as one organism among many. Although this always occurs within an *environment*, over time we have (culturally at least) become increasingly disconnected from and unconcerned with the natural world. Many of our chapters highlight moments when this growing detachment has been both mourned and challenged. And yet as we look now towards the 2030s and beyond, it is clear that our very survival as a species may rest upon our ability to (re) discover what it is to be human. Assuming a technological future dominated by increasingly sophisticated forms of artificial intelligence, our sense of purpose and our value as humans may well lie in our own nature, and our ability to recognise ourselves as organisms among many that are not. Alternatively, if societal breakdown occurs as a result of climate change, probably combined with other human-induced catastrophes, we may have to rely on our humanity towards each other as we learn to survive as organisms in a less benign environment than we have known for many millennia. Each of our chapters marks a unique contribution to the telling of this story.

The capacity for learning is not unique to humans. However, it is something we are particularly good at, when we put our minds to it, which we have been, and we have been doing for a long time. Human learning about the environment also has a long history. It's something we've been engaged in ever since we began interacting with our surroundings and thinking about the impacts, outcomes and consequences of our (inter)actions. This is still something many of us do on a daily basis. Although, unlike in the past, it's now only a minority of humans for whom that kind of learning is predominantly a matter of life and death, there are still many parts of the world where learning to guard against or avoid coming into contact with the daily reality of pathogens and toxins has to be reinforced through community-based public health programmes. Indeed, as we complete this book, everyone in the world is having to face up to the spread and consequences of the 2019 novel coronavirus, COVID-19.

In the past, such learning has accrued from lived experience and has never had much to do with schools and schooling (and colleges, universities, etc.) as we have come to know them. Historically, it has nearly always been very local to the learner and informally arranged. As a consequence, it has never had to bother with curriculum theory, syllabuses, instructional approaches, learning outcomes, accountability measures, and the like. That said, it can be plausibly argued (as we shall show) that there might well have been informal and rudimentary schemes of work, and even the very notion of curricula, as far back as the Late Palaeolithic Period (c. 10,000 BCE). Further, although the magisterial *Saber Tooth Curriculum* (Benjamin 1939) might be a 20th-century satire on the arguments for traditional v. progressive framings of the curriculum, a basis in fact when such animals[1] roamed the land is not without possibility.

Clearly, as time passed, and human communities gradually became more settled and secure, the sort of existential learning associated with living amongst large cats became only one of an increasing range of possibilities for learning. As these expanded, so did the need for a more formalised organisational structure and specialisation (i.e. schools, curricula and teachers in one form or another). So much so that, in economically developed communities at least, the opportunities for learning about environmental matters became squeezed and then marginalised. That remains the case today in the 21st century, even though many now argue that humanity again faces at the very least an environmental threat to its culture, if not to its very existence; this time because of the loss of unique habitats, species and biodiversity, the acidification of the oceans, the pollution of air and water, and now global heating and rapid climate change.

It is the case, of course, that formal teaching with a focus on the environment (usually termed environmental education) blossomed in the last half of the 20th century. This happened as our problems began to be more widely appreciated, and Rachel Carson's iconic book *Silent Spring*, in the 1960s, was one of the significant axes around which awareness turned. This resulted in local, national and international action in an attempt to focus the work of schools and universities on our absolute dependence on the natural world and the multiple jeopardy that our ways of living were subjecting us to. Teacher education was also a key focus in this with the United Nations Educational, Scientific and Cultural Organization (UNESCO) once declaring it to be the "priority of priorities". Environmental non-governmental organisations (NGOs) began to take learning by the public seriously, and often proved better at it than schools were with students. Up to now, this environmental education has proved more durable in universities than in schools. This is, we think, in large part, because of the academic freedom enjoyed by lecturers and researchers, and the real-world influence on what is studied in higher education at a time of rapid climate change.

There is another (almost parallel) element to our story. This concerns a long tradition of writing and activism with a focus on conservation (and sometimes preservation) of habitats and land areas deemed to be of intrinsic or social value. Much of this output in English is from the USA, although all cultures with a written tradition exhibit it. Prominent writers include Ralph Waldo Emerson, David Henry Thoreau,[2] John Muir and Aldo Leopold. Through such writings it's possible to trace developing concern about what human economic activity was doing to the planet's ability to support life and make it worth living. Some of this thinking had a basis in religious teachings, with sacred texts being used selectively by both sides of what sometimes became a charged debate. This writing continues today but is just as likely to come from international NGOs and United Nations (UN) agencies, as from prominent public intellectuals. It's also now more likely (though not certain) to have a focus on environmental quality and literacy – and even, sometimes, specifically on learning.

The 1970s saw the start of focused international activity to address the problems being caused by human economic development. There were two strands to this. One focused on environmental education with meetings in Carson City, Belgrade, Tbilisi, and Bonn. The other focused on human development and the environment with meetings in Stockholm, Rio and Johannesburg. The first culminated in the UN Decade of Education for Sustainable Development (UNDESD), with the Tbilisi declaration as a prominent landmark. The other resulted in the Paris Agreement, with the World Conservation Strategy, the Brundtland Commission, Agenda 21, and the Millennium Development Goals along the way. We shall explore why, despite attempts at convergence, these were largely parallel tracks. They have, to a degree, now come together as the Sustainable Development Goals that embody an agenda for change by 2030 where much learning will be necessary for success.

The book is divided into three parts, with a set of appendices:

Part I: Past historic – up to the end of the 1950s

Part II: Present imperfect – from the publication of *Silent Spring* to today

Part III: Future possible – looking ahead

Notes

1 For further details see: tinyurl.com/ybfgtj43
2 Henry David Thoreau was born David Henry Thoreau, named after his mother's brother, David Thoreau. He began to call himself Henry David after he finished his college studies, but never officially changed his name.

Further reading

Benjamin, H.R.W. (1939). *Saber Tooth Curriculum, Including Other Lectures in the History of Paleolithic Education*. New York: McGraw-Hill.

PART I
Past historic

1

HUMANS BEING

"For our prehistoric ancestors all learning was probably environmental and success was measured by survival."[1]

This book highlights individuals and social movements that down the ages, whether for reasons of morality, aesthetics or survival, have sought to remind us of our connections to the natural world. This begs the question of when it was first felt necessary to provide such reminders, which in turn prompts us to consider when it was that we apparently stopped being "natural" ourselves.

This is more than simply humans changing the environment; we can observe many creatures doing that, if mostly unconsciously. The shifting grazing patterns of wildebeest in East Africa supress woody plants thus ensuring that the Serengeti is ideal for, well, grass. Perhaps we can point to our hunter-gatherer ancestors as examples of humans living harmoniously as part of nature. Yet even this is questionable, for as the historian Yuval Harari points out, *Homo sapiens* may have been responsible for wiping out other human species such as *Homo neanderthalensis* (Harari 2011), although this "replacement" was not wholesale as recent studies show significant genetic traces in modern humans that suggests some interbreeding took place (Bae, Douka & Petraglia 2017).

Our ability to make fire may be seen as an early "unnatural" breakthrough that no other animal has achieved. Again, archaeological evidence suggests that even our primitive ancestor *Homo erectus* was making use of fire and thus probably cooking food over a million years ago (Berna et al. 2012). But it would be stretching a point to suggest that these early humans had become as detached from the natural world as we are.

Perhaps it is our very human nature that distinguishes us from the rest of nature. No less an authority than Charles Darwin suggests that it is our moral sense, our ability to care for others whom we do not know, even those from other species, that "affords the best and highest distinction between man and the lower animals" (Darwin 1879:151). But even here we encounter higher-order mammals behaving altruistically, witness dolphins helping beleaguered swimmers to safety. Yet Darwin was on to something: human intelligence, with its capacity for self-awareness and abstract thought, sets us apart from other animals. It is likely that humans are unique in the way in which we are able to live in a dual reality – that is the objective reality of our physical world and a constructed reality based on our imaginations and our interpretations of the world.

Harari argues that it is our ability to both (a) behave flexibly and (b) do so in large numbers that has enabled us to become so dominant, and that this was only made possible by our ability to go beyond basic communication and to tell stories. This unique combination of abilities is a product of our thinking processes and also the way in which we communicate these. In the early 1930s the Soviet psychologist Lev Vygotsky highlighted the role of language as an essential tool in human development. It is this that allows us to convey ideas across time and space so that each new generation can start from where its predecessors left off. While many creatures can communicate with what we might recognise as a basic language, as far as we can tell no other species has a language with such versatility that it can convey abstract thought. For as long as humans have had language, we have been learning cumulatively, not just from our own experiences but from each other's, including from those whom we could never have met. For humans, therefore, it seems that there is no going back to some pre-aware, more natural state.

As our opening quotation states, for our prehistoric ancestors all learning was probably environmental and success was measured by survival. More recent accounts of learning among indigenous peoples show that many essential skills were acquired through play, and that work and play were not distinct categories (Gray 2013). Social bonds were reinforced through ritual storytelling, no doubt deeply rooted in local environments and providing an interconnected view of the world that included humans in the cycles of life. This may be as close to natural as we will ever get because any possibility of aligning human interactions with the environment alongside those of other intelligent animals came to an end with the advent of agriculture. Occurring some 10,000 to 12,000 years ago, agriculture and the domestication of livestock was perhaps the most significant step ever taken by humans in terms of modifying the global landscape. In a timeline of momentous developments that might include language – fire – agriculture – writing – gunpowder – printing – the Industrial Revolution – the atomic bomb – digitisation, it could be argued that agriculture stands apart as the most momentous of all in that it changed our direction rather than simply accelerating an existing process. If humans changed nature through agriculture, then the next most significant leap may be the development of artificial intelligence if that is allowed to change human nature. We return to this in our closing chapter.

The cultivation of crops, first in evidence in the Middle East but occurring independently across Asia and later in South America, allowed societies to establish more complex social structures. While these complex settlements and social structures develop in fixed locations, the anthropologist Hugh Brody (2000) argues that agricultural societies are in fact more mobile and nomadic than hunter-gatherers (who tend to stay grounded in one area) because of the continuous migration to new land driven by population increase among agricultural communities. Maintaining such complexity requires more than verbal communication and so systems of writing emerged based on earlier hieroglyphic forms, again in the Middle East, with writing found in Sinai dating from between 1850 BCE and 1550 BCE, and similarly dated cuneiform script in Mesopotamia. The Phoenician alphabet from around 1100 BCE is the oldest verified alphabet to date and was followed by independent developments of scripts in the Indus Valley and within the Zhou dynasty of China. The significance of writing is that it demands literacy, which calls for some form of structured education, albeit for an elite class of scribes. Henceforth it became a matter of record that learning no longer focused primarily on the objective, bio-physical realities of our environment but on the means by which we convey our interpretations of the world including the myriad human concerns that we deem important at any given time. Indeed, we might frame this book as a history of attempts by people to convey stories to the rest of us that cut through our constructed worlds in order to remind us of the significance of our objective reality.

Note

1 John Smyth. (1995). Environment and Education: a view from a changing scene. *Environmental Education Research*, 1 (1), 1–20.

Further reading

Bae, C.J., Douka, K. & Petraglia, M.D. (2017). On the origin of modern humans: Asian perspectives. *Science*, 358 (6368). Web link: tinyurl.com/w3qjfpm

Berna, F., Goldberg, P., Horwitz, L.K., Brink, J., Holt, S., Bamford, M. & Chazan, M. (2012). Microstratigraphic evidence of in situ fire in the Acheulean strata of Wonderwerk Cave, Northern Cape province, South Africa. *Proceedings of the National Academy of Sciences of the United States of America*, 109 (20). Web link: tinyurl.com/qp8tq3p

Brody, H. (2000). *The Other Side of Eden: Hunters, Farmers and the Shaping of the World*. London: Faber & Faber.

Darwin, C. (1879). *The Descent of Man*. 2nd edition. London: John Murray.

Gray, P. (2013). *Free to Learn: Why Unleashing the Instinct to Play Will Make Our Children Happier, More Self-Reliant, and Better Students for Life*. New York: Basic Books.

Harari, Y.N. (2011). *Sapiens: A Brief History of Humankind*. London: Penguin.

2

PLAYING AND LEARNING IN THE MESOLITHIC

"As knowledge was cumulative, specialised and could be stored, even maintenance of the status quo required its transmission between generations."[1]

For our prehistoric ancestors all learning was essentially environmental and success was measured by survival, and Gough (2017) argues that education in some form or other (i.e. structured learning) became both possible and necessary because of this. Wilson (2019) makes much the same point. She examined a methodological framework for identifying how young people in the Mesolithic Period (c. 10,000 BCE) spent their time in post-glacial Northern Europe.

As Wilson noted, young people were obviously present in these groups and she asked: how can we shed light on what they got up to? Wilson argued that children must have spent at least some of the time learning (if only informally), as the need for learning is implicit if family groups and societies are to endure. She said that much of this learning must have been about the environment, thus preparing them for their economic and social roles in later life: acquiring skills and competences, as we might put it today. Wilson was speculating, of course, as the archaeological record does not speak volumes about the youth of pre-history, but she set out a plausible case that there must have been a formalisation of learning to some degree, as the induction of the young into the evolving skills necessary to stay alive and thrive needed to happen. She suggested that there might have been a sort of monitorial system where those children who knew more instructed the others,[2] and that there might have been learning through play. This is plausible and Högberg (2008) has examined the potential for identifying play and children's imitation in the archaeological record including a case study of a flint knapping area for Neolithic axe production in southern Sweden that identifies a child's activity area. Högberg writes about theoretical and methodological assumptions behind play, imitation and its identification. See also Lillehammer (2015), who examined the idea of play as an analytical tool towards considering the child's world from an archaeological perspective, arguing that technological and methodological advancements have improved the abilities of archaeologists to study childhood. Co-incidentally, recent accounts of learning among indigenous peoples show that many essential skills were acquired through play, and that work and play were not distinct categories (Gray 2013). They still aren't.

As such learning evolved, whether from play or not, it always accrued from lived experience and never had much to do with institutions (schools, colleges, universities, etc.) as we have come to know them. Historically, it has nearly always been very local to the learner and informally arranged.[3] As a consequence, it is impossible to imagine that it ever had to bother very much with curriculum theory, syllabuses, instructional approaches, learning outcomes, accountability measures, and the like. However, if there were valuable skills and dispositions to be learned, then that suggests, one way or another, that there were purposes, a conceptual frame, outline schemes of work, and favoured pedagogies. This sounds like a curriculum of sorts.

But if there were a curriculum, there would also inevitably have been disputation about it, even if it were not quite what Benjamin (1939) suggested in the magisterial *Saber-Tooth Curriculum*.[4] Although this is a 20th-century satire on the arguments for traditional v. progressive framings of the curriculum, actual arguments in the Mesolithic about timeless knowledge versus practical skills for the future, which lie at the heart of Benjamin's work, are plausible. Interestingly, however, Benjamin did differentiate between children's play and adults' work. This is his description of how the first thought of education come to the hero of the story, New-Fist-Hammer-Maker:

> He saw these children at the cave entrance before the fire engaged in activity with bones and sticks and brightly colored pebbles. He noted that they seemed to have no purpose in their play beyond immediate pleasure in the activity itself. He compared their activity with that of the grown-up members of the tribe. The children played for fun; the adults worked for security and enrichment of their lives. The children dealt with bones, sticks, and pebbles; the adults dealt with food, shelter, and clothing. The children protected themselves from boredom; the adults protected themselves from danger.

If only, New-Fist thought, he might get these children to do things that would lead to more and better food, shelter, clothing and security, he would help the tribe to have a better life. Thus, having set up an educational goal, New-Fist proceeded to construct a curriculum for achieving it. To cut a long story short, this was all a great success with the young learning useful skills. Time passed, and all was well.

However, a changing climate eventually brought environmental problems for the tribe and new technologies had to be developed for it to survive. This meant that the skills that the children had been learning were no longer of practical value and were essentially now only historical curiosities. As a consequence, curriculum disputation ensued as some began to argue that it was the new, very practical skills and knowledge that should be taught and not the outmoded ones. As one young radical argued:

> You will have to admit that times have changed. Couldn't you please try these other more up-to-date activities? Maybe they have some educational value after all? ...

The old men would have none of it. If you were educated yourself, they sneered, you'd know that the essence of true education is timelessness. It is "something that endures through changing conditions like a solid rock standing squarely and firmly in the middle of a raging torrent".[5]

Such arguments continue today in the face of contemporary changes in the climate.

Notes

1 Gough (2017).
2 For more about the monitorial system, see: lancasterian.org
3 In some ways, the picture Wilson paints seems like today's forest schools and outdoor classrooms.
4 This was set in much earlier times than the Mesolithic. See: tinyurl.com/yaefxlfm
5 What the elders thought of play as a mode of learning was never recorded.

Further reading

Benjamin, H.R.W. (1939). *The Saber-Tooth Curriculum, Including Other Lectures in the History of Paleolithic Education*. New York, NY: McGraw-Hill.

Coates, J.K. & Pimlott-Wilson, H. (2019). Learning while playing: Children's Forest School experiences in the UK. *British Education Research Journal*, 45 (1), 21–40.

Gough, S. (2017). Education after Sustainability. *Global Discourse*, 7 (1), 131–145.

Gray, P. (2013). *Free to Learn: Why Unleashing the Instinct to Play Will Make Our Children Happier, More Self-Reliant, and Better Students for Life*. New York: Basic Books.

Högberg, A. (2008). Playing with Flint: Tracing a Child's Imitation of Adult Work in a Lithic Assemblage. *Journal of Archaeological Method and Theory*, 15 (1), 121–131.

Lillehammer, G. (2015). 25 Years with the 'Child' and the Archaeology of Childhood. *Childhood in the Past*, 8, 78–86.

Wilson, P. (2019). Towards a methodological framework for identifying the presence of and analysing the child in the archaeological record, using the case of Mesolithic children in post-glacial northern Europe. In David Jacques and Graeme Davis (Eds), *Stonehenge a Landscape through Time 2*. Oxford: Peter Lang.

3

EARTH MOTHER – MOTHER EARTH

"Glastonbury is a small eccentric country town where many people come to live an internalised womb-like life for a time."[1]

The idea of the Earth Mother remains a powerful one for many people; anyone doubting it should spend an afternoon in Glastonbury, where this and many other myths thrive. The Earth Mother conjures up images of unconditional care, nurture and protection, and modern archaeological interpretation suggests that some early human societies worshiped the Earth for its fertility and bounty. Viewing the human-Earth relationship as analogous to the baby-mother bond captures the essential concept of humanity's utter dependence on the Earth.[2] Whether the Earth was viewed as a living being (an early Gaia theory perhaps) or not, is another matter.

This idea of Mother Earth or Earth Mother is very old and is widespread across the world's cultures. Mother Earth embodies nature, motherhood, fertility, bounty and creation (and, it has to be said, sometimes also destruction). The Mother Earth idea still appeals to people today and is especially beloved of some environmentalists who can find in the Earth a spiritual quality that might otherwise be missing from their lives. As we note elsewhere, if the Earth is the source of all goodness and nourishment, should it not be respected, nurtured and generally looked after?

A popular modern view is that early societies were matriarchal with the worship of a nurturing Earth Mother goddess being part of this. Others, however, see this as just a projection of current worldviews onto the past with this being seen as a useful counterpoint to the patriarchal organisation that has dominated most human societies over modern times. But the reality of a nurturing Earth does not necessarily imply a matriarchal structure and organisation. For some who think it does, however, such pre-societies represented a golden age characterised by harmony, peace, a natural wisdom and a light tread on the Earth. Another myth.

Many cultures had the Earth Mother concept. What follows is a small representation of such examples:

Cybele – The Earth mother of the central Anatolian region. She represented the fertile Earth and was goddess of all nature. She was called Sibyl in Greece and was thought, under divine inspiration, to be able to utter prophesies.[3]
Demeter – In Greek mythology the goddess of the harvest, whose name originally meant Earth Mother.[4]
Ninhursag – The Sumerian mother goddess: the Mother of the Gods and Mother of Men for her part in creating both divine and mortal entities.[5]
Maimata – The Hindu Rigveda calls her the divine female power, Mother Earth.[6]
Iusaaset – The grandmother of all the Egyptian gods who is associated with creation. She is usually pictured as a woman wearing a horned vulture crown.[7]
Hathor – The Egyptian goddess of love, femininity, joy, motherhood and fertility was pictured as a cow, or as a woman with cow horns or ears. She was celebrated as a Mistress of Life.[8]

Closer to home (for us at any rate), and in the present day, there is Brigit[9] who originally was goddess of the ancient British Kingdom of Brigantia. Brigit regenerates the forces of nature at the end of each winter. As Kathy Jones notes, Imbolc[10] (halfway between the Winter Solstice and the Spring Equinox) is Brigit's festival,[11]

> in which the Light of Illumination from Her perpetual flame is brought into a darkened room, heralding the coming of spring. Small honey and barley cakes are eaten and milk drunk in Her honour. On the first day, the ears of corn from the Lammas Corn Doll are planted in the ground and the dried stalks are burned, the flame releasing the life back into the earth. The ashes are spread upon the ground.

In a similar vein (but not necessarily connected)[12] and usually on Twelfth Night, wassailing takes place. This ceremony stimulates the first stirrings of life to help it emerge from winter's grip and ensure that the next season's fruit crop (usually apples and pears) will be good.[13]

That such connections between fertility and the Earth from the ancient past remain active even in a developed capitalist economy (and they are much more extensive across the world) shows the hold that myth and tradition still have on us and on our need for connectedness to nature.

Notes

1 "Priestess of Avalon", Kathy Jones describes Glastonbury thus: "Glastonbury is a small eccentric country town where many people come to live an internalised womb-like life for a time. It may be nine or eighteen months or more, before they are reborn, sometimes spewed out from the body of the Great Mother. As the Goddess in the landscape is ever-pregnant and continuously giving Birth, this process is repeated in the many

different areas of life for those who live here. Visitors too are catalysed into new ways of living by the touch of Her Life-Giving Body." See: tinyurl.com/y4fp9l7x.

2 It is easy to see why the idea of Earth Father never had much meaning in societies where child rearing was a mostly (if not wholly) female task.

3 See: goddess.org/vortices/notes/cybele.htm

4 See the Ancient History Encyclopedia: ancient.eu/demeter

5 See the Ancient History Encyclopedia: ancient.eu/sumer

6 R.V. 1.164.33 See: ancient-wisdom.com/earthmother.htm

7 See the Ancient History Encyclopedia: tinyurl.com/yycnb98h

8 See Egyptian Gods and Goddesses: tinyurl.com/y7r7wjqb

9 Pronounced breed.

10 Pronounced emolc.

11 And linked with Candlemas. It is one of the four Celtic Fire Festivals. See: tinyurl.com/pv3uxar

12 Nick Jones of World Heritage Trails notes: "The origins of 'wassail' ('be you healthy') appear to be a post-Norman version of an Anglo-Saxon greeting (not a toast). The apple and cider connections are of earlier origin. Apple trees existed in pre-history on/near the Somerset levels, and apple wood was used, with other material, to make the Sweet Track (3807BCE) across the marshes near Shapwick. Further, Ynys Avalon means Isle of Apples in Old Welsh/Cornish/Breton. Whilst the alignment of some Early Neolithic tombs in Ireland coincide with sunrise at Imbolc, St Brigit is early Irish Christian, and the two appear to have been linked, perhaps in the same way that Christmas Day supersedes celebration of the Winter Solstice. New cultures appropriate existing traditions."

13 See White Dragon at: tinyurl.com/y5wkxccw

Further reading

Jones, K. (n.d.). *Remembering the Nine Morgens: the nine sisters of Avalon.* Web link: kathyjones.co.uk/category/books

Lovelock, J. (1979). *Gaia: A New Look at Life on Earth.* Oxford: Oxford University Press.

4

IN THE BEGINNING

"Fiat lux."[1]

Gaia was the god of the Earth in ancient Greek mythology who created herself out of chaos at the dawn of creation. Although Gaia had a reputation as something of a troublemaker amongst the gods, she was viewed as the mother of everything, including all the other Greek gods. All mortal creatures were born of her flesh. The ancient Greeks saw the Earth as a flat disc surrounded by a river with the solid dome of heaven above. The disc rested on, and was inseparable from, Gaia's breast. As we saw in the previous chapter, this idea of Mother Earth (or Earth Mother) is ancient. It embodies nature, motherhood, fertility, and bounty, as well as creation.

A creation myth is an account of how the Earth and/or the wider cosmos formed, and how humans (and sometimes other organisms) arose. Such myths usually tell a story about the coalescing of matter out of disorder, a general fuzziness, or even nothing at all to form the material reality we are familiar with. Some see these as conveying a literal truth – this is how it really happened – whilst others read them as just a story rooted in ancient culture – often religiously grounded. However, amongst the latter, some might see such myths as conveying important socio-political messages about the relationships between humans and the Earth, and hence about how to live. They are all, one way or another, about nature.

Creation myths tend to share a range of features. For example, they can be found in nearly all known religions. They tend to have a storyline involving gods, humans or animals who can switch between these forms. They are set in a distant, unspecified past. They address fundamental questions of identity and set out a worldview.

There are numerous classifications of creation myths, for example:[2]

From chaos – Judeo-Christian-Islam, Sumerian
Emergence – Navajo, Hopi, Mayan, Zuni

World parents – Babylonian, Maori, Greek
The cosmic egg – Hindu, Buddhism
Earth diver – Cherokee, Romanian
Ex nihilo – Egyptian, Maori

From the perspective of the relationship between humans and nature, the Genesis story is particularly interesting because of its influence in those places where the Industrial Revolution and the Enlightenment emerged. The story is a familiar one. Here are verses 1 to 5 in the King James version of the Bible:[3]

> In the beginning God created the heaven and the earth.
>
> And the earth was without form, and void; and darkness *was* upon the face of the deep. And the Spirit of God moved upon the face of the waters.
>
> And God said, Let there be light: and there was light.
>
> And God saw the light, that *it was* good: and God divided the light from the darkness.
>
> And God called the light Day, and the darkness he called Night. And the evening and the morning were the first day. …

So far, so good, but it's verses 26 to 28 where the issues arise:

> And God said, Let us make man in our image, after our likeness: and let them have dominion over the fish of the sea, and over the fowl of the air, and over the cattle, and over all the earth, and over every creeping thing that creepeth upon the earth.
>
> So God created man in his *own* image, in the image of God created he him; male and female created he them.
>
> And God blessed them, and God said unto them, Be fruitful, and multiply, and replenish the earth, and subdue it: and have dominion over the fish of the sea, and over the fowl of the air, and over every living thing that moveth upon the earth.

Instructions to "subdue" and "have dominion over" in this story make it plain that all had been divinely established for the benefit of humanity. Even after the expulsion from Eden and the terror of the Flood, the instruction was reissued:

> And God blessed Noah and his sons, and said unto them, Be fruitful, and multiply, and replenish the earth.
>
> And the fear of you and the dread of you shall be upon every beast of the earth, and upon every fowl of the air, upon all that moveth *upon* the earth, and upon all the fishes of the sea; into your hand are they delivered.[4]

Nature, in other words, and according to Biblical authority, is a resource and by implication one that replenishes itself; and all for the benefit of humanity. Pushing this line suited the early Christian Church's purposes as it wanted to have no truck with Earth-grounded paganism or spirituality, all of which diluted its core message about a divine creator and the Trinity.

Porter (2000:299) quotes two 18th-century views on this which might have been early arguments for the modern travel industry:

> Nature was a resource, "principally designed", asserted the Cambridge divine and Newtonian popularizer Richard Bentley, "for the being and service and contemplation of man". "We can, if need be, ransack the whole globe" maintained his fellow physico-theologian the Revd William Derham, "penetrate into the bowels of the earth, descend to the bottom of the deep, travel to the farthest regions of the world, to acquire wealth, to increase our knowledge, or only to please our eye and fancy."

In the view of many, this cornucopian perspective has served some of humanity very well, but the biosphere itself quite badly.

Notes

1 Let there be light. Genesis 1.3. Was this just the light of the sun or was it the light of reason as well?
2 This is a confusing area with overlapping categorisations. What is presented here is just one of many possibilities. See: tinyurl.com/rapty8a
3 You will find this verse here: tinyurl.com/jqja6rz
4 For this verse, see: tinyurl.com/sz9eg9g 2

Further reading

Porter, R. (2000). *Enlightenment: Britain and the Creation of the Modern World*. Harmondsworth: Penguin Books.
von Franz, M.-L. (2001). *Creation Myths*. London: Shambhala Books.

5

VIRGIL'S *GEORGICS*

"I'll begin to sing of what keeps the wheat fields happy, under what stars to plough the earth, and fasten vines to elms."[1]

Neither of us was privileged enough to attend the sort of school where Virgil's *Georgics* was on the curriculum and so we never got to study them, or forced to copy them out a hundred times or so when we'd broken the rules.[2] But we knew about them through the exploits of Billy Bunter who regularly suffered in these ways.[3]

The *Georgics* [4] was written in four parts between 37 and 29 BCE. Its outward theme is farming and rural life and it glorifies many aspects of country living. It is a realistic text. As the Classical Literature website notes: "The Georgics' scenes are real and vivid, allowing the reader to feel the sights, sounds, and textures of the ancient Italian landscape."[5]

Virgil wrote the *Georgics* partly as a response to his patron's request for a poem praising Roman agriculture and presenting it as a valuable and patriotic endeavour. He structures the poem so that agriculture and the natural world can be read as metaphors for life. Its political messages convey idealised pictures of a farmer's life: living lightly on the Earth, in harmony with the natural world, through hard work, which underpins the greatness of Italy, rewards come, despite disappointments and setbacks along the way, resulting in peace and contentment; and all fully approved of by the gods.

Part 1 of the poem focuses on growing arable crops and on the weather. It stresses the importance of human work to success or failure and ends with a description of the terrible social and economic consequences of the murder of Julius Caesar. Part 2 deals with the growing of trees, particularly olives and vines, and contrasts natural (biological) and artificial (human) methods. A prominent theme sees agriculture accurately portrayed as a human struggle against a hostile natural world. There is also a long section praising Italy. Part 3 concerns the rearing of livestock, particularly the selection of breeding stock. Part 4 focuses on bees, wasps and hornets, and on beekeeping. In this, bees are viewed, ironically, as exemplars of an ideal citizenry and described as "little Romans".

Although clearly a didactic poem, the *Georgics* was unlikely ever intended by Virgil as a practical user manual. However, the poem's didactic nature endured. Ruth Abbott, leader of a Cambridge University Eighteenth-Century and Romantic Studies M.Phil programme, argues that many of the most popular poems of the long 18th century were primarily instructive and were inspired by the lessons in farming outlined by Virgil. They explained to readers how to do things like "rear sheep, make cider, go hunting, know oneself, look at a landscape, grow a cucumber, or correct despondency".[6]

The programme also explores how the *Georgics* influenced 18th-century poems providing guidance on how to cultivate landscape "physically through forms of 'improvement', politically through acts of interpretation, and morally through the imagination". One such poem was Oliver Goldsmith's *The Deserted Village* (1770).

The legacy of the *Georgics* has lasted down the centuries, and not just in curricula or agricultural instruction. It has been wide-ranging in a cultural sense, as the blurb for a 2019 Reworking Georgic conference noted:

> The influence and spirit of "georgic", as a genre or mode – named for Virgil's *Georgics*, the primary classical model – can be seen across western art and culture: from medieval and early modern almanacs to eighteenth-century formal georgic poems, from pre-Raphaelite social paintings to the new nature writing of the twenty-first century. Writers and artists have used the georgic mode to explore a broad range of significant themes, including nationhood and empire, industry, the experience of war, the cultivation of the self, and humans' relationships with the natural world.[7]

It is doubtful, however, that the *Georgics* will have anything to tell us about how world agriculture will have to change if it is to adequately feed a still-growing human population – or about how the population will adapt to a changing agriculture. Certainly, farmers, in these post-Malthusian and Anthropocene[8] times, would be unlikely to find Virgil's idealised pictures of a farmer's life any more convincing than they probably were when they were first written. Moreover, farmers are now required to perform a difficult balancing act: growing nutritious food, preserving soil quality, carbon and biodiversity, satisfying a range of pressure groups and activists, surviving international competition, and justifying protectionist tariffs, all the while being dependent on public subsidy. Virgil had none of this to contend with, and would not have been able to imagine it, although he did have the social chaos induced by civil war.

Notes

1 Opening lines of *Georgics*, Part 1. See Poetry in Translation: tinyurl.com/yytwnfuf

2 One of us did study Latin though, at least for a while, but never ascribed to the old adage which holds that "Latin is a language as dead as dead can be. It killed the ancient Romans, now it's killing me."

3 Billy Bunter, Tom Merry, Jimmy Silver and everyone else at Greyfriars school were the creations of Frank Richards (Charles Hamilton; 1876–1961) and published in *The Magnet*, a weekly boys' story paper (1908–1940), and in post-World War II novels published from 1947 to 1965. They also featured in 1950s BBC TV programmes.

4 The title came from *Georgicon*, Greek for agriculture or working the land.

5 See: Classical Literature: ancient-literature.com/rome_vergil_georgics.html

6 See Poetry and Knowledge: Georgic and Didactic Verse in the Long 18th Century, at: tinyurl.com/y2wuggsl

7 See Reworking Georgic at: tinyurl.com/y57er24m

8 We explore the Anthropocene in our penultimate chapter.

Further reading

Fallon, P. (2004). *Virgil Georgics*. Oxford: Oxford University Press (Oxford World's Classics).

Hagenstein, E.C., Donahue, B. & Gregg, S.M. (Eds.) (2012). *American Georgics: Writings on Farming, Culture, and the Land*. New Haven, CT: Yale University Press (Yale Agrarian Studies Series).

Virgil. *The Georgics*. Poetry in Translation. Web link: tinyurl.com/yytwnfuf

6

HOW THE GREENLAND NORSE CHOSE

"Nothing beside remains. Round the decay
Of that colossal Wreck, boundless and bare
The lone and level sands stretch far away."[1]

Jared Diamond published *Collapse: How Societies Choose to Fail or Survive* in 2005 with a revised and expanded edition in 2011. Diamond says that the book was his attempt to understand why so many past societies failed after making huge investments (capital, technological, human and social) over long periods, noting a well-documented role for environmental factors in many of these. One of his chosen subjects was the Norse settlement on Greenland in the early part of the 2nd millennium CE, and we focus on this because it seems clear that a changed climate played a key role in what happened to the people there. Our purpose in writing this chapter is to wonder what the Norse population was learning as it turned colder and more stormy, with both working and living conditions becoming much more difficult and hazardous.

We know that Norse explorers first settled on Greenland's west coast in the 980s. Another more south-easterly settlement was established over the next hundred years, but the entire population never exceeded the low thousands. The climate was mild (given the location) when they first arrived and remained so (with some fluctuations) until the late 13th century.

Their settlements were substantial, with a cathedral, churches, large houses and numerous farms, barns, byres and storehouses. They raised sheep, goats and cattle, grew fodder, and hunted caribou and seals. Archaeological evidence from middens shows that the settlers had a significant Harp and Hooded seal diet from the outset, and human skeleton analysis shows that it had become around 80% seal by the time the settlements ended.

The Norse were never self-sufficient, importing grain, iron, wine and other commodities, and what we would think of as luxury goods. Diamond's richly detailed account of their life there paints a picture of an integrated, essentially feudal, economy. He says that five adjectives characterise the society: communal, violent, hierarchical, conservative and Eurocentric, which had been carried over from ancestral Icelandic and Norwegian societies. There was trade both internally between settlements and individual farms, and externally with Iceland and the European mainland. They traded with Europe in furs, falcons, walrus ivory and skin, and even live polar bears. But they were vulnerable to both economic and climatic shocks.

Around 1350/1360 the south-easterly settlement was reported abandoned, and Inuit begin to appear near the Norse areas, settling along the coastline. From this point, the trade between Norway and Greenland gradually declined, and the last written record of the Norse was brought on the last ship to sail back to Norway in 1410. Sometime between 1480 and 1500 the Norse involvement in Greenland came to an end, and European explorers, when they returned in the 1720s, found only ruins.

But, what were the Norse? Were they farmers who, as the weather changed, found their way of life increasingly impossible, and as their animals died, so did they? If so, was this because they failed (or declined) to learn from the Inuit about how to adapt to change? The Inuit had been successfully living around the northern Greenland coast since the early 1200s and had a marine-based diet and distinctive lifestyle. A counter-view amongst archaeologists, summarised by Folger (2017), is that the motivation for the Norse settlements wasn't farming, but ivory trading.

What is certain is that the climate cooled because of a volcanic eruption in Indonesia which spewed ash and sulphur dioxide into the high atmosphere, partially blocking sunlight. This resulted in more Arctic sea ice and greater and more frequent ocean storms, and there were dramatic changes to prey populations. Despite these difficulties, the Norse remained for at least another 100 years after the climate began to change, and they continued developing their settlements. European trade became increasingly difficult, however, because of the increasing sea ice.

Moreover, as well as being affected by climate change, Folger (2017) says that the Norse settlers were also victims of globalisation and a pandemic, as around the same time the market for walrus ivory collapsed. This was, he says, in part because African elephant ivory became available again when the Crusades came to an end, but also because of the Black Death which reduced population and hence demand. For example, the pandemic halved the Norwegian population in 1349/1350. Barrett et al. (2020) also suggest that the Norse were probably finding it increasingly hard to find walrus tusks because of the climate changes.

So, did the Norse abandon the settlements (gradually or otherwise) or did they stay there to die out? Or was it a bit of both? Opinion seems divided. Although walrus hunting persisted, it likely would have been increasingly difficult and hazardous because of the sea conditions as it involved travelling long distances. Seal hunting, though more local, would also have been riskier and it might not have taken much loss of life to have dramatically disrupted the home economy and their ability to endure. Folger reports that the ruins hint at an orderly departure with there being no evidence of conflict with the Inuit. Although the Norse were a literate people, there is no written record to support this or any other conclusion.

We don't know anything about how aware they were of the developing nature of their predicament; in all likelihood it was probably not very much. Gough and Scott (2007:119) argue that the Norse were faced with phenomena about which they not only didn't know, but also that they didn't know they didn't know. They say that enquiry into such matters would have been impossible for the Norse in part because the appropriate techniques were not available to them, but also because they had no means of knowing how to enquire. They would know that there had been change, but not why, and could not have known whether or how this might continue. Despite our own uncertainties today, we are at least better off than they were in this respect.

In the end, as climatic conditions grew worse for the Norse they would have been faced with a choice of continuing to live as they were, or changing.[2] This comes down to how important a continuing connection to their essentially European culture was for them. Gough and Scott (op. cit.) wondered whether it was really the environment that caused problems for the Norse, or whether they caused the environment to be more of a problem by how they chose to live. Diamond lists a number of ways in which they didn't help themselves, adding (2005:275):

> The Norse were undone by the same social glue that had enabled them to master Greenland's difficulties. … the values to which people cling most stubbornly under inappropriate conditions are those values that were previously the source of their greatest triumphs over adversity.[3]

And Lynnerup (quoted by Folger) compares the Norse with European settlers to North America for whom there "was never any question of … becoming nomadic and living off buffalo".

This was all a long time ago and many questions remain, but the combination of conditions that prevailed then (climate change, pandemics, economic collapse and cultural conservatism) all feature in our world today. How *we* choose to handle all this in the longer term remains to be seen.

Notes

1 Three lines taken from Shelley's *Ozymandias* (1817). The complete poem forms a preface to Diamond's *Collapse* (2005/2011).
2 The Inuit experienced the same climate change, but their mode of living enabled them to move south to avoid the worst of the changes.
3 The Norse importation of stained glass for their places of worship suggests a long commitment to European Christian values. In the end prayer did not prove an effective response to a very secular climate.

Further reading

Barrett, J.H., Boessenkool, S., Kneale, C.J., O'Connell, T.C. & Star, B. (2020). Ecological globalisation, serial depletion and the medieval trade of walrus rostra. *Quaternary Science Reviews*, 229 (1).

Diamond, J. (2005/2011). *Collapse: How Societies Choose to Fail or Survive*. New York, NY: Viking Penguin.

Folger, T. (2017). Why did Greenland's Vikings Vanish? *The Smithsonian Magazine*. March. Web link: tinyurl.com/top986h

Gough, S.R. & Scott, W. (2007). *Higher Education and Sustainable Development: paradox and possibility*. London: Routledge.

7

SCIENCE AND THE ECOLOGICAL IMAGINATION

"The imagination is most accurately excited by familiar things, which are well enough known to be picked up from a world where they lie at random, taken apart, reconstructed and redesigned, and put in exact places where they are appropriate."[1]

An understanding of the four laws of thermodynamics is fundamental to appreciating the limits to the usefulness of energy and therefore to the seriousness of the environmental and sustainability issues facing humanity. One of the most accessible, if rather basic, expositions of the first and second laws was that set out by the satirists Flanders and Swann on their 1964 recording, *At the Drop of Another Hat.* [2] In this, Flanders explained to Swann what he might have learned at school about heat, work, entropy and the death of the universe if the curriculum hadn't been so specialised.[3] As it is, Flanders alleged, Swann not only was ignorant of the second law, but didn't know the first law either. The satire lies not in the science, but in the fragmentation of culture and curriculum.

In his introduction to the song, Flanders cites C.P. Snow's 1959 Rede lecture, *The Two Cultures and the Scientific Revolution.* [4] Snow's thesis was that the cleavage of the intellectual life of Western society into the sciences and humanities was a hindrance to solving the world's problems. As Flanders put it:

One of the great problems of the world today is undoubtedly this problem of not being able to talk to scientists because we don't understand science [and] they can't talk to us because they don't understand anything else.[5]

A *Nature Physics* editorial on this problem, which is particularly pronounced in England, noted:

The fissure had opened more than a century earlier, with the coming of the industrial revolution, and grew as the body of scientific knowledge developed. … scientists had declared themselves different from the traditional literary culture, which largely ignored them.

Snow blamed it on a highly specialised education, but also on something more fundamental: an intellectual superiority and disdain for the sciences which, ironically enough, is reflected, he said, in similar feelings towards applied science and engineering from (pure) science itself.[6]

But there is more to it than this. In her 2015 doctoral thesis on "Science and Nature in the Medieval Ecological Imagination", Jessica Rezunyk (p.12) noted that Snow's arguments were "merely a continuation of a public (yet cordial)[7] debate between Matthew Arnold and TH Huxley established in the previous century".[8]

This was, *prima facie*, about curriculum, but really about culture. In a series of debates, Arnold defended the centrality of literature and classical languages in education. He claimed that science lacked a connection to human culture or experience in its search for mere facts; it was literature, he claimed, that gave access to the underlying values of human nature. Huxley was against narrow specialisms of any kind and saw science as an essential part of a culturally balanced education. Rezunyk (2015:14) writes that:

Huxley identified medieval ambivalence toward study of the natural world as one of the main reasons to be skeptical of the heavy-handed role of classical approaches to education that had been established in the Middle Ages. Such approaches, Huxley argued, were inevitably influenced by the Church in ways that specifically excluded any inclination to explore the natural world through science and had no place in the nineteenth-century classroom.

His view was that science should be free from the influences of religion (and politics) and from the prejudices of narrow-minded humanists as well.

Rezunyk (p.15) notes the superficiality of these descriptions of medieval learning, but says that it is "clear from this exchange between Arnold and Huxley that religion and medieval culture have played historically significant roles in the debate between literature and science", and she concluded that they "cannot be disregarded in any contemporary examination of the perceived divide".

A key aspect of her argument is that a medieval understanding of human culture was inextricably connected to perceptions of the natural world, and that the medieval imagination was able to establish a connection between science and the humanities that became far less common from the late 17th century as the Enlightenment engendered philosophical and political shifts that swept away existing worldviews.

According to Rezunyk, science, as we broadly understand it today, existed before the scientific revolution of the 16th and 17th centuries although it wasn't an academic field. However, medieval thinkers placed a high value on knowledge that could be gained through observation of the natural world.[9] She quotes A.N. Whitehead (1925), who emphasised the historical dependence of science on the depiction of natural objects in art.[10] Even earlier, according to Wolpert (1998), Thales[11] had looked for explanations of phenomena within nature rather than the agency of the gods.

Rezunyk says that our location of the study of nature within the sciences and the study of culture within the humanities has created a gap between nature and culture that keeps their methodologies and even vocabularies largely separate. Her examination of medieval literature shows some of the ways that the sciences and humanities can overlap to create spaces for the study of nature and culture. Framed within the ecological analyses of G. Evelyn Hutchinson, and using the methodology of studies in science, technology, and society (STS) developed by Bruno Latour, the dissertation demonstrated how scientific topics can be approached from a literary perspective and how, in turn, literature can be read scientifically.

Some 60 years on from Snow, 140 years after Huxley and Arnold, and around 300 years after the Enlightenment, this rift (and competition) remains with us. It can be seen in how we think, and in particular in English secondary schools with their compartmentalised study of the natural sciences, social sciences, and arts and humanities.[12] In these schools, the hapless student is largely left to their own devices to see connections, make sense of gaps, and imagine possibilities.[13]

And yet, the heavily human-influenced natural world is inexorably interconnected. This is why we need an education that critically examines our self-induced ecological predicament in a holistic way that stimulates both our imagination and concern, and leads to social and political action.

Notes

1 This quote is used by Jessica Rezunyk, a medieval studies scholar in chapter one of her dissertation. This is her footnote to the quotation: "G. E. Hutchinson, known in the scientific community as the 'Father of Ecology,' was acutely aware of how the natural world could impact language. This summary of his philosophy of ecology can be found in the introductory pages of Hutchinson's first publication, The Clear Mirror, where his detailed descriptions combine environmental and cultural observations (3–4). This characterization of the imagination marks Hutchinson's transition from nature to culture in the text." Hutchinson is describing one aspect of the creative process.

2 You can hear the song and its introduction in full here: tinyurl.com/mz6g7j2

3 Both Donald Swann and Michael Flanders attended Westminster School and Christ Church, Oxford. Swann studied modern languages but Flanders wasn't allowed to complete his degree because he was disabled by polio during the Second World War.

4 The full text of the lecture is available on panarchy.org. See: tinyurl.com/y3dzn7ds

5 Snow wrote the following which is part of a *Nature Physics* editorial: "A good many times I have been present at gatherings of people who, by the standards of the traditional culture, are thought highly educated and who have with considerable gusto been expressing their incredulity at the illiteracy of scientists. Once or twice I have been provoked and have asked the company how many of them could describe the Second Law of Thermodynamics. The response was cold: it was also negative. Yet I was asking something which is the scientific equivalent of: Have you read a work of Shakespeare's?" This quoted in *Nature Physics* (2009). See: tinyurl.com/y66hh58e

6 See our chapters on the English Romantic poets and 18th-century (sustainable) development goals for related comment.

7 This was before social media coarsened scholarly (and other) interchange.

8 In her PhD she explored the intersections between nature and culture in medieval literature and art with particular focus on Chaucer's *House of Fame*, the 13th-century French Bible Moralisée and Langland's *Piers Plowman*, and identified ways in which these medieval writers used science and nature as tools for communication in the humanities.

9 Rezunyk says that evidence of these observations can be found not only in academic textbooks and treatises, but also in religious and literary works.

10 Whitehead writes: "The rise of Naturalism in the latter Middle Ages was the entry into the European mind of the final ingredient necessary for the rise of science. It was the rise of interest in natural objects and in natural occurrences, for their own sakes. The natural foliage of a district was sculptured in out-of-the-way spots of the later buildings, merely as exhibiting delight in those familiar objects [...] The simple immediate facts are the topics of interest."

11 Thales (of Miletus 624–545 BCE) was a pre-Socratic Greek philosopher who is recognised as the first individual in the West to engage in what we'd recognise today as scientific enquiry.

12 Geography sits uncomfortably astride these, trying to be common ground.

13 Those from a background where discussion of issues is commonplace at home are better served, but only, arguably, if the many facets of this divide are represented.

Further reading

Ashby, E. (1958). *Technology and the Academics*. London: Macmillan.

Atkins, P. (2007). *Four Laws that Drive the Universe*. Oxford: Oxford University Press.

Editorial. (2009). *Nature Physics*, 5 (5), 309.

Page, J.W. (2011). Susanna Blamire's Ecological Imagination: Stoklewath; Or the Cumbrian Village. *Women's Writing*, 18 (3), 385–404.

Rezunyk, J. (2015). Science and Nature in the Medieval Ecological Imagination. *Arts & Sciences Electronic Theses and Dissertations*. Web link: openscholarship.wustl.edu/art_sci_eds/677

Roos, D.A. (1977). Matthew Arnold and Thomas Henry Huxley: Two Speeches at the Royal Academy, 1881 and 1883. *Modern Philology*, 74 (3), 316–324.

Snow, C.P. (1998). *The Two Cultures*. Cambridge: Cambridge University Press.

Whitehead, A.N. (1925). *Science and the Modern World*. Lowell Lectures. New York: The Free Press.

Wolpert, L. (1998). *The Unnatural Nature of Science: Why Science Does Not Make (Common) Sense*. Cambridge: Harvard University Press.

8

FRANCIS BACON AND THE INTERROGATION OF NATURE

"Bacon, like Moses, led us forth at last,
The barren wilderness he past,
Did on the very Border stand
Of the blest promis'd Land,
And from the Mountains Top of his Exalted Wit,
Saw it himself, and shew'd us it."[1]

Francis Bacon (1561–1626) is sometimes described as the first post-Renaissance thinker. He was a lawyer and statesman who became Attorney General (1613–1617) and then Lord Chancellor of England (1617–1621) under King James I. His career ended in disgrace in 1621 when a parliamentary committee charged him with corruption.[2] He is not really remembered for scandal, however, but for his philosophy and the modern scientific thinking for which this paved the way. Bacon was also the founding inspiration and later figurehead for the Royal Society[3] which was formed in the 1660s by a group of natural philosophers and physicians who had first met in the mid-1640s to discuss Bacon's ideas.

Bacon has been called the father of empiricism and his thinking was always a struggle against tradition. He argued for a rejection of the dominant views about the acquisition of knowledge which originated with Aristotle, and with the Classical Greek world more generally. His 1620 book, *Novum Organum* (1620), set out an approach to the generation of knowledge about the natural world based on observation of the world and experimentation, rather than using just logic and deductive methods, arguing from first principles that was then widely practised, particularly in universities. What Bacon found lacking in these established ways of thinking was a theory of science which could be widely applied to natural history and philosophy.

Bacon opposed the humanistic interpretation of Aristotle's work with its emphasis on logical reasoning through syllogism[4] and the dialectical exchange of propositions.[5] He criticised Cambridge University in particular for placing too much emphasis on such approaches. He rejected the idea that what we experience through our senses (perceiving things as they appear to be) represents an understanding of things as they actually are. He defined his alternative procedure as one "which by slow and faithful toil gathers information from things and brings it into understanding" (Farrington 1964:89). This was based on real-world knowledge carefully and progressively built up. It is the scepticism at the heart of this method that makes Bacon a key thinker in the evolution of the scientific method.[6] In particular, Bacon (1620, op. cit.) warned against four false assumptions "which are now in possession of the human understanding, and have taken deep root therein", which he called idols.[7] These were:

1.   Idols of the Tribe – fallacies in human nature where "human understanding is like a false mirror, which … distorts and discolours the nature of things by mingling its own nature with it".
2.   Idols of the Cave – misconceptions in individual thinking because of prejudice.
3.   Idols of the Marketplace – problems from communication when "words plainly force and overrule the understanding, and throw all into confusion, and lead men away into numberless empty controversies and idle fancies".
4.   Idols of the Theatre – errors "which have immigrated into men's minds from the various dogmas of philosophies".

Bacon was, of course, not alone in finding the status quo unacceptable. His greatest strength, perhaps, was his ability to communicate his ideas at a time when they would fall on receptive ears; it was this that put science on the cultural map. To be a Baconian in the years that followed his death was to see the value of, and therefore to use, observation and experimental approaches which is something we now take for granted. A good example is Newton's ground-breaking work on optics. But Bacon's inductive approach has not survived in its original form, and these days it is likely to be hypothetico-deductive approaches that are widely used where ideas and theories about the world are tested through experiment.[8] Voltaire said that Bacon's *Novum Organum* was the scaffold that enabled the new philosophy to be constructed. Once erected, however, the scaffold was no longer needed.[9] Nonetheless, his work on logic and the organisation of scientific enquiry has had a long-lasting legacy.

Bacon thought it important not just to contemplate nature but to use it. His real interest was in unlocking nature's secrets. That is, to discover nature's laws so that these could be used for the benefit of humanity. He thought that the state should fund such inquiry to release this understanding which would then give rise to material and economic benefits. Given that the Stuart kings were usually short of cash, this was never done. At least part of Bacon's motivation was his understanding that the progress being made in commerce and the practical arts was not being seen in relation to our understandings of the natural world. There was a need, as we might put it today, for new ways of knowing for a new world. Although it's true that Bacon began the modern theorising of science, it's also the case that his rhetoric and imagery were probably just as significant as the inductive method itself. For example, he used nature to compare approaches. In his 1607 book, *Cogitata et Visa*, he compared deductive logic to the creation of a spider's web from silk drawn out of the spider's own body. By contrast, the bee represents the empiricist, which by means of his inductive method, collects natural matter and turns it into honey (i.e. useful knowledge).

Bacon used extensive and vivid metaphors to describe his inductive approach into discovering nature's secrets. He wrote about bringing nature into subjection, grabbing nature by the forelock, and about nature needing to be pressed and forced under art. It is easy to understand how, as a successful lawyer used to courtroom practice and needing to get evidence from witnesses, he might have found using the legal imagery appealing. As Stephen Pumfrey (2009) notes, "I think Bacon did think of the process by which a male natural philosopher probes the secrets of nature, which was normally thought of as feminine, as very much like an aggressive prosecutor probing a reluctant, recalcitrant female witness". This gendered imagery of abuse and violation lasted a long time. Boyle used it, and Davy wrote, for example, of taking the veil away from nature.

This language jars now even though we no longer regard nature as feminine, other than in phrases such as Mother Nature. Bacon was right about one thing, however: nature does not reveal its secrets easily at all.

Notes

1 Quoted in the introduction to Thomas Sprat's *The History of the Royal-Society of London* (1667). See: tinyurl.com/yxdrov4m. It is one of those odd coincidences that another Bacon (the Franciscan, Roger Bacon 1220–1292) had also been an early philosopher of science who was preoccupied with method. His fate was also to fall foul of authority. Francis Bacon is regarded by some as the man who really wrote the Shakespeare plays. For a witty exploration of this, see the Richmal Crompton story *William Holds the Stage*.
2 There is much debate about why Bacon confessed to these accusations when what he had done (accepting gifts from litigants) was common practice.
3 The Royal Society's motto is *nullius in verba* – take nobody's word for it – an expression of a determination to withstand the domination of authority and to verify all statements by an appeal to facts determined by experiment. See royalsociety.org. According to John Aubrey, Bacon died in 1626 from pneumonia brought on during his experiments exploring the effects of cold on the preservation of meat.
4 For an exploration of syllogisms see: philosophyterms.com/syllogism. Probably the most famous example is this: All men are mortal (major premise); Socrates is a man (minor premise); therefore Socrates is mortal (conclusion).
5 For an exploration of dialectics see: tinyurl.com/y3bld2ep
6 Voltaire introduced Bacon's ideas to a French audience in 1773 describing him as the father of the scientific method. His non-metaphysical approach to science became more influential in France than Descartes's dualism. For a comparison of Descartes's approach with that of Bacon, see: tinyurl.com/y5ntwdlu
7 The idols are explored here: tinyurl.com/y5dad3dx
8 For more on hypothetico-deductive approaches see: tinyurl.com/y365tnnx
9 See Voltaire's *Essay on Bacon*: tinyurl.com/y4m49fpa

Further reading

Bacon, F. (1607). *Cogitata et Visa*. Web link: tinyurl.com/r5cjkcf

Bacon, F. (1620). *Novum Organum*. Web link: tinyurl.com/y3but727

Farrington, B. (1964). *The Philosophy of Francis Bacon*. Liverpool: Liverpool University Press.

Merrill, T.W. (2008). Masters and Possessors of Nature. *The New Atlantis*, 19, 91–107. Web link: tinyurl.com/y4bneqml

Pumfrey, S. (2009). *BBC In Our Time. Baconian Science*. Web link: bbc.co.uk/programmes/b00jdb6c

Stanford Encyclopedia of Philosophy. (n.d.) Francis Bacon. Web Link: tinyurl.com/y328kfzn

9

DESCARTES, THE WORLD AND THE METHOD

"How do you get along with French people? Oh very well! Yessss. So do I, yes! So does Mrs. E! I like them. They think well, don't they? I mean, be fair: Blaise Pascal, Jean Paul Sartre, Voltaire, René Descartes."[1]

René Descartes (1596–1650) was the son of a French lawyer. He studied philosophy, science, and mathematics at the Jesuit school of La Fleche but left France in 1618 to fight in the Thirty Years War. He continued to study when he could but became dissatisfied with the unsystematic approach to science (based on prior authority rather than observation) that characterised all previous work.[2]

In 1619 he said that he dreamt of a set of rules – a universal method – for reasoning and seeking the truth of things, which he attempted to write down on his return to Paris in the 1620s. In the early 1630s, he wrote what is known as his physics book: *Le Monde* (The World). This took a Copernican, heliocentric perspective, and drew on a mechanistic metaphor to explain the working of the world. Descartes stopped publication, however, when Galileo ran into predictable trouble with the Inquisition for writing similar things.

In its place, Descartes published three non-Copernican essays together with a preface: the *Discourse on Method*.[3] This is Nordgren's (1998) summary of Descartes's rules for his method, which tells us what we need to do in order to know anything with certainty:

1. accept as "truth" only clear, distinct ideas that could not be doubted
2. break a problem down into parts
3. deduce one conclusion from another
4. conduct a systematic synthesis of all things.[4]

Descartes based his approach to science on this deductive method of reasoning.

This was a radical rupture with previous philosophical thinking as, in Descartes's words, it was a "practical philosophy" that enabled humanity to discover "the force and actions of fire, water, air, stars, the heavens, and all the other bodies that surround us as distinctly as we know the different trades of our artisans".[5] That is, it gave us power over nature; the power to bring material benefits and "enable us to enjoy, without any pain, the fruits of the earth and all the goods to be found there".[6] The most fundamental good to come out of this, Descartes thought, would be medicine based on scientific knowledge, as he saw the betterment of human health and the realisation of well-being as the foundations of all other material benefits that such knowledge would bring. He underlined his good intentions by emphasising that he was "strongly opposed to any other projects, especially to any that can help some people only by harming others".[7]

Descartes understood the essentially collective nature of such enquiry and the need for a means of public communication. Like von Humboldt after him, he asked those reading his work to send him their experimental results.

There is a grand bargain at the heart of what Descartes was proposing; a bargain that lay at the heart of the Enlightenment. On the one hand there is a freedom (granted by society) to research and communicate; on the other there is the promise of material benefits and lives more free from want and disease than ever before. The contrasts between what this proposes and what is promised by the Christian Church (and many other religions) could not be starker: a materially better life now in the world consciously experienced, as opposed to a speculative promise of an eternity in paradise. And yet there is an imbalance in all this; whilst society can directly influence the science (and scientists) through laws, regulation and public opinion, science (and scientists) can only influence what human societies do indirectly, for example by advice to government through evidence to inquiries, and through expert committees. Indeed, at the time of writing, we are keenly aware of the work of scientific advisory committees helping the UK government decide how to handle the COVID-19 virus. The key word here is advisory, as public policy rests with democratically accountable politicians and not with the scientific community.[8]

This could be one of the reasons that, despite the manifold success of the Enlightenment project, it hasn't quite worked out so well. In many parts of the world, the paradisiacal delusion continues to exert a strong grip, and life is still nasty, brutish and short for many people.[9] And then there's global warming and catastrophic climate change which may well bring the Cartesian world crashing down.

Cartesian ideas, boosted by liberal democracies, have been a success in many ways, and there was an inevitability about the emergence of the Cartesian view,[10] just as it was inevitable that somewhere there would be an industrial revolution. It was 17th- and 18th-century Western Europe that provided the necessary conditions for this mastery of nature to prosper and no apology is necessary.

Notes

1 Interview with the Pepperpot ladies in a Monty Python sketch. The Pepperpots revered French thinkers but had no time for the Germans: "RUBBISH! Rubbish! Emmanuel Kant! Bloody 'Ego posits itself!' My foot! Nietzsche?! HAH!". See: tinyurl.com/y2zx2j5b for further explication.
2 This criticism did not apply to mathematics. For a comparison of Descartes's approach with that of Bacon, see: tinyurl.com/y5ntwdlu
3 Its full title was: *Discourse on the Method of Conducting One's Reason Well and Seeking Truth in the Sciences*. See: tinyurl.com/y5h7njrn. Part 5 of this is a summary of the unpublished *Le Monde*. This begins: "Good sense is the best shared-out thing in the world; for everyone thinks he has such a good supply of it that he doesn't want more, even if he is extremely hard to please about other things." This was not Descartes agreeing with this proposition, of course, but his pointing to the difficulty of influencing firmly held views. Almost 400 years on, this phenomenon is still with us. He subsequently published *Meditations* in 1641, the *Principles of Philosophy* in 1644 and the *Passions of the Soul* in 1649.
4 What Descartes wrote is available here: tinyurl.com/y5ntwdlu
5 Quoted in Merrill (2008).
6 Quoted in Merrill (2008).
7 P.31 of Nordgren's translation: tinyurl.com/y5ntwdlu
8 There are also cases where national leaders wilfully ignore scientific evidence in pursuit of their preferred policies, thus breaking faith with the Cartesian deal. Examples include President Donald Trump in the USA, Brazil's President Jair Bolsonaro and President Alexander Lukashenko of Belarus.
9 This was Thomas Hobbes's memorable way of picturing the human experience. See: tinyurl.com/y4wujqnj
10 Readers will have noted that we have managed to write this chapter without any mention of the soul, a notion which preoccupied Descartes. This omission, given the nature of this book, is deliberate.

Further reading

Grayling, A.C. (2006). *Descartes: the life and times of a genius*. London: Walker Books.
Merrill, T.W. (2008). The New Atlantis Masters and Possessors of Nature. *The New Atlantis*, 19, 91–107. Web link: tinyurl.com/y4bneqml
Nordgren, T. (1998). *The Scientific Methods of Rene Descartes and Francis Bacon*. Web link: tinyurl.com/y5ntwdlu

10

ROUSSEAU WROTE *EMILE*; PESTALOZZI MADE IT REAL

"… the important thing is to understand what you're doing rather than to get the right answer."[1]

Rousseau (1712–1778) had a difficult start in life. His mother, Suzanne, died of a postpartum infection days after his birth, leaving Jean-Jacques and his elder brother François, to be raised by their clockmaker father and a maternal aunt in and around Geneva. The varied and seemingly haphazard nature of his education had a deep influence on the young Rousseau; indeed his entire life is characterised by non-conformity, switched allegiances and relocations, often to avoid a legal scrape or strained relationship.

In the same year that Rousseau published his *Social Contract* (1762), which inspired revolutionaries across Europe, not least those involved in the French Revolution, he also published his thoughts about education and child rearing in the form of a semi-fictitious work called *Emile, or On Education*. Like Comenius and Descartes before him, Rousseau deplored the abstract nature of religious instruction and the reduction of science to mere words rather than any observation or experiment. In an age when education was dominated by exercises in memory, Emile's upbringing would be a reversal of virtually everything that was common practice.

Emile is divided into five books; the first three take Emile from birth to age 15, the fourth deals with adolescence, while the fifth covers the education of Sophie, the girl Emile would ultimately marry. Sophie's role was subordinate to Emile; she was clearly educated to be governed rather than to govern.[2]

For Rousseau education is seen as a developmental process, driven by natural curiosity. Children learn from their surroundings but due to the malign influence of corrupt society they often fail to grow into virtuous adults. He therefore advocates educating the child in the countryside, away from society, guided by a guardian who does not teach as such but offers a series of learning experiences, some quite elaborate and contrived. Ultimately the aim is to learn how to live righteously and to learn how to learn:

> The thing is, not to teach him knowledge, but to give him a love for it, and a good method of acquiring it when this love has grown stronger. (Rousseau 1889:131, translation by Worthington)[3]

Rousseau used "natural" education in two senses. Firstly, he meant all that is not human (although in this he included our bodies as distinct from our minds). He was also referring to the psychological development of the child, all the time paying close attention to their capacity to grasp more complex ideas as they grow older. He saw society as having a similar "natural" evolution, from the savage state to the modern day, with civil society being an imitation of nature because it "models itself on the inflexibility of natural law" (Allan 1937:206–207). This attempt at a unifying theory has not withstood scrutiny over time.

There is a clear distinction to be made between nature and human influence; the opening sentence of Book One reads:

> Coming from the hand of the Author of all things, everything is good; in the hands of man, everything degenerates. (Rousseau 1889:11, translation by Worthington)

This is a proto-Romantic view that appears to contradict Rousseau's ideas about humans originally being a part of the natural world. That said, he would be the first to claim that nature itself is full of paradoxes. As he says when advising teachers to "lose time" in order to promote the learning process, "I prefer paradoxes to prejudices" (op. cit.:57).

This natural learning involves an emphasis on play; an echo of learning processes observed in indigenous societies (Gray 2013). We are told that a child who does as he pleases will be less bothersome than one who is constantly beset by restrictions:

> The meaning of these rules is, to allow children more personal freedom and less authority; to let them do more for themselves, and exact less from others. (op. cit.:33)

As Emile reaches his twelfth year in Book Two, there are still no punishments; instead curiosity is led by careful questioning and real-life experiments. Learning about the solar system, for example, begins with observations of the sunset and the sunrise from the same place and at different times of the year. No books are introduced at this stage, rather the focus is on education *of* and *through* the senses[4] and relies on the child's ability to draw inferences from these experiences.

No attempt is made to inculcate reason; for Rousseau reason is an end in itself, not the means:

> The noblest work of education is to make a reasoning man, and we expect to train a young child by making him reason! This is beginning at the end; this is making an instrument of a result. (op. cit.:52)

In Book Three Emile's attention is again drawn to natural phenomena but he doesn't learn in any didactic sense, rather he must discover science for himself. It is the teacher's role to ask questions, to encourage reasoning but not to provide ready answers; authority is no substitute for reason. When Rousseau describes a beautiful sunrise over a rural vista, he insists that Emile's experience should not be smothered by the teacher's words:

> Carried away by such a sight, the teacher is eager to impart to the child his own enthusiasm, and thinks to arouse it by calling attention to what he himself feels. What folly! The drama of nature lives only in the heart; to see it, one must feel it. (op. cit.:52)

Thus, the child develops their own attachment to nature and will acquire the skill to express their feelings in their own time. Foreshadowing the work of 20th-century psychologist (and fellow Genevan) Jean Piaget, Rousseau's observation that the ten-year-old child "does not readily generalize or conceive of abstractions" (op. cit.:156) corresponds with Piaget's concrete operational stage of child development.

Rousseau's ideas were shared with many contemporaries, including Frederick the Great in Prussia. Emmanuel Kant claimed to have been influenced by him, and he was close to the Scottish philosopher David Hume for a while before they fell out irrevocably. In terms of turning Rousseau's occasionally fanciful ideas into reality, perhaps the most significant figure is that of Swiss educationalist Johann Heinrich Pestalozzi (1746–1827).

Pestalozzi was deeply influenced by *Emile*, a copy of which was always by his bedside, and he saw Rousseau as the man who "made the child its own creature again and restored education to children and to human nature" (Soëtard 1994:298). In common with his hero, Pestalozzi placed a special emphasis on spontaneity and self-activity. Children should not be given ready-made answers but should arrive at answers themselves following a period of quiet, concrete observation that he called *Anschauung*. His followers described this in various ways: "from the known to the unknown, from the simple to the complex, from the concrete to the abstract" (Smith n.d.). Like Rousseau, he saw this as a psychological method of instruction that would follow the laws of human nature.

Perhaps Pestalozzi's greatest contribution was to apply these ideas through practical experiments. He started with a scheme to educate orphans and poor children on his farm at Neuhof. Like Rousseau, he was also a great believer in young people learning a trade, both as a rigorous form of learning and as an insurance policy against an uncertain future. Ultimately the scheme foundered, largely as a result of poor management. He then published his ideas in the form of a four-volume story, *Leonard and Gertrude*, which helped to raise his profile and provided a few donations to support his work. He remained tenacious in conducting his experiments at various locations despite frequent setbacks due to war and other political upheavals.

Pestalozzi's influence grew after the publication in 1801 of *How Gertrude Teaches Her Children*, which takes the form of letters to a friend. This outlined his thinking about pedagogy and the need to achieve balance across the domains of hands, heart and head. Finally in Yverdon in 1805, he established a school that became famous throughout Europe. The German philosopher, Johann Friedrich Herbart, who came to know Pestalozzi while tutoring in Switzerland, termed this pedagogy the "Pestalozzi Method". The instruments or techniques themselves, however, were not as important as the underpinning philosophy of "freedom with autonomy" (Soëtard 1994:303).

The impacts of all this work were far reaching. The ideas of Rousseau and Pestalozzi are still apparent in constructivist, learner-centred forms of education such as the Montessori and Reggio Emilia[5] approaches. Two siblings credited with founding the formal education of infant teachers in Britain, Charles and Elizabeth Mayo, were inspired by Pestalozzi (Charles spent three years at Yverdon). The German educator Friedrich Fröbel also studied under Pestalozzi before establishing his own school in Blankenburg, Germany; that school became known as *kindergarten*. The teachers, or kindergarteners, were taught to recognise the individual needs and capabilities of each child from the earliest years and to educate them through their own experiences in order to become integrated and whole people (Froebel 1967). The term kindergarten is used widely today, even if the approaches may not always faithfully reflect the original ideals.

Both Rousseau and Pestalozzi are seen as laying the foundations of Romanticism, which arose in response to the rapid industrialisation that was about to sweep across Europe. Meanwhile, much to the irritation of commentators and policy makers who would prefer a less progressive, more instrumental approach to education, their ideas on education remain stubbornly influential.

Notes

1 This is part of Tom Lehrer's introduction to his song "New Math", recorded in 1965, in which he parodies the introduction by the US Government of conceptual approaches to teaching arithmetic. Rousseau would likely have loved Lehrer's demolition of such an approach. See: tinyurl.com/oowxurr

2 Rousseau's view of female education and the subordinate role he ascribed to women attracted well-founded criticism even among his contemporaries, most notably from the British philosopher and feminist, Mary Wollstonecraft and the French writer, Louise d'Épinay.

3 Eleanor Worthington's translation is here: tinyurl.com/tp7ywe2

4 In Book Two of *Emile* Rousseau lists the senses as being: touch; sight; drawing; geometry; hearing; voice; taste.

5   The Reggio Emilia approach in early years education was developed by Loris Malaguzzi and participating parents in this northern Italian region. The approach conceives of children as born with a "hundred languages" or different means of expression. The approach seeks to develop those languages, e.g. through the arts, whereas traditional teaching tends to reduce them to just one or two.

Further reading

Allan, D, (1937). Nature, Education and Freedom According to Jean-Jacques Rousseau. *Philosophy*, 12 (46), 191–207. Web link: jstor.org/stable/3747139

Froebel, F. (1967). Outline of a plan for founding and developing a kindergarten. In I.M. Lilley (Ed.), *Friedrich Froebel: A selection from his writing* (117–119). New York, NY: Cambridge University Press.

Gray, P. (2013). *Free to Learn: Why Unleashing the Instinct to Play Will Make Our Children Happier, More Self-Reliant, and Better Students for Life*. New York, NY: Basic Books.

Rousseau, J.-J. (1979/1762). *Emile or On Education*. Translation by A. Bloom. New York, NY: Basic Books.

Rousseau, J.-J. (1889/1762). *Emile or On Education. Extracts*. Translation by Eleanor Worthington. Boston, MA: Heath & Co.

Smith, M.K. (n.d.). Johann Heinrich Pestalozzi: pedagogy, education and social justice. In *The Encyclopaedia of Informal Education*. Web link: tinyurl.com/o4cdhlr

Soëtard, M. (1994). Johann Heinrich Pestalozzi. *Prospects: the quarterly review of comparative education*, XXIV (1/2), 297–310.

11

THE 18TH-CENTURY (SUSTAINABLE) DEVELOPMENT GOALS

"To be SOLD, A FINE NEGRO BOY, of about 4 feet 5 inches high, Of a sober, tractable, humane Disposition, Eleven or Twelve years of Age, talks English very well, and can Dress Hair in a tolerable way."[1]

The year 2015 saw the Paris Agreement on climate change and the launch of the UN Sustainable Development Goals (SDGs)[2] whose main purpose is to transform people's lives and to establish sustainable development. The 17 goals (and 169 targets) are shown in Appendix 4. They cover our most pressing contemporary issues: poverty, hunger, equality, energy, clean water and sanitation, biodiversity, climate change, economic growth, sustainable cities, and responsible consumption, as well as strategies such as education and justice.

The goals and targets are not perfect, and some feel they do not go far enough to address the root causes of our global problems. Others argue that the 17 goals are not all equally important and that we need to prioritise those which will have the most impact. Both these points reinforce the need for us to think critically about the goals and understand how to influence and effect change.

The title of this chapter is, of course, misleading. There were no sustainable development (or other international) goals in the 18th century. The idea of sustainable development was yet to come, there were no UN committees or international NGOs to agree such a list, and no means of global communication to bring them about. Reading accounts of life and work in the early 18th century and reflecting on today's SDGs, shows how much social progress has been made over 250 years, and how much is still to do.

In the western hemisphere, the middle of the 18th century was in some ways a time like our own since World War II. Rapid socio-economic change (and environmental and ecological damage) was being wrought by a developing Industrial Revolution and there was a population shift to cities. The factors underpinning these developments were technological change in agriculture and industry, a rising population, the ready availability of venture capital,[3] manual and animal labour giving way to machines driven by water and then by coal power, and the development of new tools. These made for huge productivity increases, a general increase in disposable income and the creation of wealth that was very unevenly distributed.

That said, had it been possible, which development goals might have been identified in the 18th century? Whilst this is a subjective business, our choice is set out here:

An end to slavery. There were ~10,000 slaves in England when slavery was declared illegal in 1772; most were domestic servants. But slavery continued in British overseas colonies and profits continued to flow.[4] It took 44 years before parliament abolished the trading of slaves in the UK and across the Empire, and a further four before the East India Company issued regulations to prohibit the transport of slaves into Company territory.

Extending the franchise. Parliament was utterly unrepresentative, and there had been calls for universal adult male suffrage and other reform in 1647 by the Levellers and left-wing, liberal Puritans such as John Lilburne.[5] A renewed call was made in 1772 but it wasn't until the 1832 Reform Act that even 16% of adult men got the vote.[6]

Social exclusion. The mid-17th-century Clarendon Code saw Corporation, Conventicle, Uniformity, and Test Acts restrict public office to practising members of the Church of England. The legislation affected membership of the civil service, universities, the law, school teaching, and preaching. Most acts were repealed in 1828. The poor were largely excluded as well owing to their lack of education and opportunity. Women were generally speaking excluded from most things outside marriage and the domestic sphere.[7]

Child labour. After 1740 the population began to rise steadily,[8] because of a reduction in infant mortality and an expansion of public health measures. These affected most social classes. But poor children had always worked, and their expanding numbers in urban areas were attractive to mill, mine and factory owners for whom they represented a cheap, compliant, readily available (and replaceable) workforce.[9]

Environmental damage. The Industrial Revolution had devastating local consequences for the natural environment. In addition to exhaust gases and soot being vented into the air and the release of chemical pollutants into waterways, giving rise to air and water pollution and ill health, there was a depletion of natural resources, especially wood. England's coverage by forest fell to around 6% in 1800. Industrial development and damage were not confined to urban areas, as contemporary poetry and art recorded.[10]

Rich and poor. It was, as now, a time of extremes with a huge disparity in wealth ownership and in earnings. The old aristocracy and squirarchy had land (a great source of wealth) and entrepreneurs were newly rich through business and enterprise. Those at the bottom, however, were increasingly exchanging rural (hand to mouth) subsistence living for urban (week-to-week) wage penury. In between, there was a rise of a skilled lower-middle class who could survive economically and expect more of life.

Working and living conditions. For many, these were characterised by capricious employers, long work hours, poor wages, no job security, a lack of safety, child labour, insanitary and polluted streets, cramped living quarters, diets lacking protein, fruit and vegetables, and the prevalence of disease.

Literacy. England's literacy rate grew from 45% in 1700 to 63% at the end of the century.[11] Schools emerged slowly against resistance from government in England.[12] Not everyone was keen on the poor being able to read about complex ideas and think for themselves, just as now not everyone across the world thinks girls should have a good education. When state education eventually emerged, it was mostly of a limited utilitarian kind, although as Porter (2000:74) notes: "The reading eye can never be blinkered."[13]

Notes

1 Plumb (1950:159) quotes this advert in the *Liverpool Chronicle* (15 December 1768).
2 They follow on from the reasonably successful but less extensive Millennium Development Goals: tinyurl.com/tvxgufl
3 There are a good many histories of this period but amongst the most readable is that of Plumb (1950).
4 Although the UK was one of the first countries to do this, and the Royal Navy was very active in supressing it as sea, it should be remembered that the UK dominated the trade for very many years. Oddly, given that slavery in many forms is still with us, it does not get a prominent mention in the SDGs.
5 There's information about Lilburne here: tinyurl.com/yylrf6yq
6 All men and some women had to wait until 1918 for the vote, and finally all women got it in 1928. Calls to extend the franchise continue with campaigns to give it to 16 year olds. See: tinyurl.com/y6qs297j
7 As now, social participation by women was always possible in the upper social strata by virtue of their position.
8 England's population was ~5.2 million in 1720 and 9 million in 1800.
9 In 1788 an Act was passed which stated that no boy should be bound apprentice to a chimney sweep under the age of eight. More general Factory Acts had to wait until the 1830s.
10 For example, Cotman's picture, *Bedlam Furnace, near Irongate, Shropshire*, and de Loutherbourg's *Coalbrookdale at Night*, show the effects of heavy industry in a rural setting.
11 In Scotland it was 85%.
12 There was a complex picture of charity schools, nonconformist academies, parish schools, and Sunday Schools, together with a range of private commercial ventures. Porter (2000:78) notes that the *Salisbury Journal* (between 1736 and 1770) contained adverts for pupils placed by 200 teachers across 78 West Country towns. Scotland and Wales, by and large, had much better school provision.
13 See chapter 2 of Dickens's *Hard Times*.

Further reading

Fairer, D. (1999). Eighteenth-Century Poetic Landscapes. *The Coleridge Bulletin (New Series)*, 13, 1–18. Web link: tinyurl.com/y255q8y2

Light, A. (2014). *Common People: the history of an English family*. London: Fig Tree Penguin.

Plumb, J.H. (1950). *England in the Eighteenth Century: a study of the development of English society*. Harmondsworth: Pelican Books.

Porter, R. (2000). *Enlightenment: Britain and the Creation of the Modern World*. Harmondsworth: Penguin Books.

Thompson, E.P. (1963). *The Making of the English Working Class*. London: Victor Gollancz.

12

THE ENGLISH ROMANTIC POETS

"Let Nature be your teacher."[1]

The English Romantic[2] poets wrote from the late 18th to the mid-19th centuries and made significant contributions not just to the development of poetry,[3] but also to wider political and social change, including the realisation of greater political freedoms. Their writing also helped our coming to see humans and nature as interdependent, and to what we'd now term ecological consciousness – a state of mind that embodies a moral standpoint towards nature.

There were many such poets,[4] but six are most remembered: Blake, Byron, Coleridge, Keats, Shelley, and Wordsworth.[5] While each was distinctive, they all captured what we see as the Romantic ideals of individuality, liberty, sensibility and simplicity. Their view was that the natural world and the emotions were the places in which one found spiritual truth. Edward Hirsch[6] says that these poets each had a particular view of the natural world, and a distinctive way of describing it. They were, he says, "sometimes solaced, sometimes frightened by its alienating majesty and inhuman force". Stephanie Forward[7] argues that the Romantics highlighted the healing power of the imagination and had a conviction that people should follow ideals rather than imposed conventions and rules. They opposed the rationalism of the Enlightenment and felt a responsibility to their fellow beings.

It was particularly Coleridge and Wordsworth who planted in our minds the idea of nature as a healing and spiritual force and the redemptive powers of the natural world, and Peter Ackroyd says that they "were truly the pioneers in what has since become the 'back to nature' movement. Anyone who yearns to walk beside the sea, or to ascend a mountain, or to row across a lake, owes a great debt to these two English poets".[8] They also helped create a new way of thinking about what was beautiful, a development from dominant classical notions of form, symmetry and proportion.

Wordsworth knew nature could provide solace and comfort both at a time and place, and also in the memory. Even when we are no longer there, its landscape, vistas, geography, topography, rock, river, turf and sky are still with us, together with how we felt about them:

> But oft, in lonely rooms, and 'mid the din
> Of towns and cities, I have owed to them,
> In hours of weariness, sensations sweet,
> Felt in the blood, and felt along the heart;
> And passing even into my purer mind
> With tranquil restoration ...[9]

When Wordsworth wrote this, England was being transformed by science, technology, venture capital, enterprise and Enlightenment values – inevitably unfeelingly – from a mainly rural agricultural society to a largely urban industrial one, with deleterious effects on both land and human society. These changes are reflected in his poetry, much of which was critical of both industrialisation and urbanisation themselves, as well as the economic materialism and instrumental rationality that underpinned them. Wordsworth was anxious about the effects of urbanisation on the natural world and, later, on the opening up of that world to an influx of city dwellers via newly constructed railways.[10] His poetry also stressed the deeply felt connection between people and place. Tintern Abbey brings these ideas together. Philip Shaw[11] notes that the poem's lines:

> ... wreaths of smoke
> Sent up, in silence, from among the trees!
> With some uncertain notice, as might seem
> Of vagrant dwellers in the houseless woods,

... echo Gilpin's *Observations on the River Wye* (1782), which records furnaces (there were also ironworks) on the banks of the river consuming locally made charcoal, and smoke spreading across the hills in what was a very rural place. For the Romantics, the Industrial Revolution was ravaging the natural environment aesthetically as well as physically.[12]

Although Tintern Abbey shows that nature provides comfort and solace, it sets out the recurring Wordsworth theme of nature as inspiration and moral guide:

> ... I still
> A lover of the meadows and the woods
> And mountains; and of all that we behold
> From this green earth; of all the mighty world
> Of eye, and ear, – both what they half create,
> And what perceive; well pleased to recognise
> In nature and the language of the sense

The anchor of my purest thoughts, the nurse,
The guide, the guardian of my heart, and soul
Of all my moral being.

Finally, an essay for the Saylor Foundation argues that although there was a call for "a return, both in life and in spirit, of the emotional and natural", Romanticism, even as it reacted against industrialisation and urbanisation, was not calling for a return to older modes of living – a mythic golden age. Rather it, stressed the importance of "reconfiguring our relationship to the world – a relationship that, for many Romantics, industrialization has thrown out of balance".[13] Two hundred years on, and in circumstances that the Romantics could not have dreamt of, that reconfiguring/rebalancing message resonates all the more powerfully.

Notes

1 This line comes from Wordsworth's "The Tables Turned". See: tinyurl.com/y6xcywmo
2 The term Romantic was applied retrospectively, from the middle of the 19th century.
3 Some (see, for example: tinyurl.com/y6mu3dvo) say that the writings of Whitman or Emerson would not have happened without the influences of the English Romantics, and Jonathan Bate says that Wordsworth taught Ruskin to value Nature.
4 There were many such poets, some of whom never received much critical attention. One such was Susanna Blamire (1747–1794) who wrote, "Stoklewath; or the Cumbrian Village". Judith Page (2011) admires Blamire's prescient ecological imagination and political perspectives about a village "secluded from the metropolis and the larger world but also intimately connected to both the natural world and the human community". Available at: tinyurl.com/y39oav4o
5 Jonathan Bate says that John Clare has to be included as a Romantic poet. You can listen to Bate's Gresham College lecture here: tinyurl.com/y34s7hw6
6 Edward Hirsch writes about nature poetry here: tinyurl.com/y23pq3qc. This is extracted from his book, A Poet's Glossary. In this he takes a long view across cultures going back to the 15th century BCE to the Canaanite mythical "Poem of Aqhat" that revolves around seasonal change.
7 See her British Library essay on The Romantics: tinyurl.com/y9uds98w
8 The Romantics (BBC): bbc.co.uk/arts/romantics/intro.shtml
9 From Wordsworth's "Lines Written a Few Miles above Tintern Abbey, on Revisiting the Banks of the Wye during a Tour, 13 July 1798". Argument enough, you might think, for every child to spend as much time as possible in the natural world – something education policy makers still struggle to take seriously 200 years on, despite convincing evidence.
10 See his "Kendal and Windermere Railway: Sonnet" in the Carlisle Journal, October 26, 1844: tinyurl.com/yyem9no4
11 See his essay for the British Library on An Introduction to "Tintern Abbey": tinyurl.com/y4e88ja2
12 See Anna Seward's 1875 account of industrial rape, "O, violated Coalbrookdale", in Colebrooke Dale which Fairer (1999) discusses. It is available here: tinyurl.com/y6mu63kq
13 The Industrial Revolution and the Romantic Spirit. The Saylor Foundation: tinyurl.com/y32cfj77

Further reading

Bate, J. (1991). *Romantic Ecology: Wordsworth and the Environmental Tradition*. London: Routledge.

BBC. (n.d.). *In Our Time: The Romantics*. Web link: bbc.co.uk/programmes/p00546ws

Fairer, D. (1999). Eighteenth-Century Poetic Landscapes. *The Coleridge Bulletin (New Series)*, 13, 1–18. Web link: tinyurl.com/y255q8y2

Page, J.W. (2011). Susanna Blamire's ecological imagination: Stoklewath; Or the Cumbrian Village. *Women's Writing*, 18 (3), 385–404.

Romantic Circles. (n.d.). A refereed website devoted to the study of Romantic-period literature and culture. Web link: rc.umd.edu

13

PUBLIC EDUCATION AND THE INDUSTRIAL REVOLUTION

"The more they are instructed the less liable they are to the delusions of enthusiasm and superstition, which, among ignorant nations, frequently occasion the most dreadful disorders."[1]

The late Sir Ken Robinson's most widely watched 2018 TED talk, *Do Schools Kill Creativity?*, includes the claim that, "around the world there were no systems of public education really before the 19th century; they all came into being to meet the needs of industrialism". While there will always be much to criticise in formal education (and Robinson's call for schools to encourage creativity is a case in point), the idea that schooling follows an industrial-age, factory model of education appears to be no more than a popular myth.

Starting in Britain in the latter half of the 18th century, the first[2] Industrial Revolution is widely seen as the most important development in human history since the widespread domestication of plants and animals over 10,000 years ago. Production, initially of textiles, moved out of homes and into factories, which were mostly powered using water and then steam from the burning of coal, as were the new locomotives. Clearly this would have an impact on learning but not perhaps in the way it is commonly portrayed. As education writer Audrey Watters explains:

> industrialization is often touted as both the model and the rationale for the public education system past and present. And by extension, it's part of a narrative that now contends that schools are no longer equipped to address the needs of a *post*-industrial world. (Watters 2015)

The rise of public education in Europe did coincide roughly with the industrialisation process but relationships between these two developments are by no means clear. To begin with, the first system of universal, publicly funded education arose in rural 18th-century Prussia.

Public education had been growing in German-speaking lands since the 1600s but it was the Prussian *Generallandschulreglement* (General Rural School Regulations) circulated in 1763 that really put Prussia on the road to compulsory public education. The decree's author, Johann Julius Hecker, had already founded Prussia's first teacher training institute in 1748, an initiative supported by Frederick the Great. Hecker gave his teachers the means to cultivate mulberry trees because silk production and weaving was one of Frederick's favourite projects.[3] The 1763 decree required all parents and guardians to send their children to school from the age of five until they were 13 or 14. Hecker declared that all children would "receive the basic elements of Christianity, reading and writing, and should also be able to read and answer for whatever is contained in our approved textbooks".[4]

Frederick supported this initiative, seeing it as a means to promote economic growth, largely through agricultural projects, after the Seven Years War (1756–1763), as well as using it to employ former soldiers in public service.[5] All of this is a far cry from drilling children to become factory fodder. That said, the "Prussian model" inspired the 19th-century educational reformer Horace Mann and is the term used to describe the organised, secular mass schooling system that he promoted in the USA. Yet Watters reminds us that in the United States:

> the "Prussian model" superseded an education system that actually *did* look like a factory. The monitorial system and its variants the Lancaster, the Bell, and the Madras systems, involved schools that were housed in large warehouses – larger often than many of the nascent factories at the time – with hundreds of students in one massive classroom with one teacher. (Watters 2015)

Meanwhile in France, laws of 1806 and 1808 established the *Université*, a complete system of schools and higher education institutions. However, owing to a prolonged period of political upheaval, plans for universal education were not fully enacted until the 1880s.

As for Britain, education was not free for the poor in the 18th century. If they were lucky, as John Clare was, children attended Dame Schools or Sunday Schools. There were some calls for mass instruction to be paid for by the state, including by Adam Smith (1776) in *The Wealth of Nations* where he suggested state-sponsored instruction of the "inferior ranks", primarily as a means of reducing the risk of revolution.[6]

Fifteen years later, Thomas Payne's *Rights of Man* proposed a practical scheme for mass education up to the age of 14. Nonetheless, while industrialisation was soaking up human labour displaced by the earlier agricultural revolution, "there could be no question of establishing a system of compulsory popular education when the new factory system was insistently demanding child labour" (Simon 1974:152).

Developments in public education seemed to be taking place *despite* industrialisation and often in response to the appalling conditions facing the poor because of it. In England, for example, Peel's Factory Act of 1802 required employers to provide young apprentices with instruction in reading, writing and arithmetic. Meanwhile adult education was the focus of some middle-class radicals who established the first Mechanics' Institute in London in 1824. These soon appeared in many towns providing night-school education for working men.[7] However it was not until 1880 that the Education Act made school attendance compulsory in England for children up to the age of ten.[8]

So systems of public education did emerge during the Industrial Revolution; indeed the increased wealth that arose from the industrialisation of society helped to make this possible. This is not, however, the same as suggesting that education arose to serve industry or even mimicked it. If we examine what all this education was for, a review of key educational thinkers suggests a number of purposes:

- A harmonious world in line with God's will (Comenius)
- To improve the human condition (Descartes)
- A moral project to harmonise the interests of the child and community while developing critical thought (Locke)
- To maintain social order and serve the state and its economy (Smith; Prussian model)
- To develop the child's character and moral sense and to achieve self-mastery (Rousseau)
- Development of the whole person to satisfy their needs and achieve inner peace (Pestalozzi)

Naturally, these ideas influenced others and were interpreted in many ways. Our primary interest in all this is the extent to which these parallel developments helped to draw us closer to nature and learning about the environment.

There is a strong thread running through that list (Smith excepted) that draws on the ideas of Sir Francis Bacon; that is, developing knowledge based on an examination of the natural world, using the senses, and moving from the particular to the general. Rousseau and Pestalozzi, of course, emphasised early immersion in the natural world before encountering the social sphere. All of this would seem to have boded well for a public education system that would help learners to understand natural phenomena in considerable depth and develop their affection for nature so that it informed their lifelong moral outlook. So what happened?

One thing those educational thinkers had in common was a misplaced belief that education would (re)create society, whereas societies invariably develop education systems that reflect themselves.[9] It was just as public education started to take a foothold in modern societies that the Industrial Revolution brought about a shift from a world primarily employed in agriculture to one where people worked predominantly in urban, industrial settings. And it was just as the state was accepting responsibility for the widespread provision of education for the first time that industrialisation stimulated the economy so that it gained a huge importance relative to other areas of public concern.

While educational values, such as those of Pestalozzi, have surfaced in educational debates from time to time – and have endured in the form of alternative approaches – public education systems have tended to look the other way as they have had to serve their paymasters in government, and the country's economic interests.[10]

It would seem that the extent to which nature study or other forms of environmental education have featured in public education, at least in Britain, has become dependent on political processes. The environment has had to compete with a wide range of other concerns, not least the economy, which, from the late 18th century to the late 20th, was overwhelmingly industrial in kind. Recent shifts to a more service-oriented economic model, or a world where environmental issues are to the fore, do not yet appear to have changed this dynamic.

Notes

1 Adam Smith (1776).
2 The first Industrial Revolution (late 18th century) was driven by coal and saw the mechanisation of manufacture, particularly in the textile industry. The second (late 19th century) was powered by electricity along with gas and oil; other advances include chemical synthesis and increased mechanisation in larger factories. The third (late 1960s onwards) saw the rise of nuclear energy and electronics; miniaturisation and biotechnology are also features of this period. The fourth (late 20th century–present) is driven by communication technology (the internet) rather than a new energy source, although the rise of renewable energy is increasingly significant. The merging of physical, digital and biological spheres promises to transform systems of production, consumption, management and governance. See: tinyurl.com/gw3e4h7
3 Thanks to Frederick the Great's efforts, in 1784 Prussia produced 16,350 kilograms of raw silk but success was short-lived as Prussia lies beyond the northern boundary for successful silk culture in Europe. See: Rein (1889). A keen advocate of agrarian innovation, Fredrick also championed the introduction of the potato to help feed his people. To this day a couple of fresh potatoes are left daily on his grave at Sanssouci Palace in Potsdam.
4 For more information see: tinyurl.com/y3d2lfuhl
5 This idea recurs down the ages. See the UK's Troops to Teachers scheme: tinyurl.com/wvk5sz8
6 See the quote at the head of this chapter.
7 Few Mechanics' Institutes encouraged or allowed female members, although this changed towards the end of the 19th century. See: tinyurl.com/yy2bdfm5
8 For an excellent account of educational developments in England at this time, see the History Docs article by David Gillard: *Education in England*, tinyurl.com/y5ubn8yn
9 The struggle to use schools to change society continues. The latest manifestation is an attempt at getting climate change embedded in school curricula.
10 Exactly whose interests are being served remains a considerable bone of contention. In capitalist economies it's the owners of capital who are usually criticised for getting in excess of their fair share, hence the calls for higher taxation and redistribution. In old-style communist ones, it was elite politicians and bureaucrats who always had special access to goods and services, but no amount of taxation reform could prevent this.

Further reading

Rein, J.J. (1889). *The Industries of Japan: Together with an Account of its Agriculture, Forestry, Arts, and Commerce*. London: Hodder and Stoughton.

Robinson, K. (2008). *TED Talk: Do Schools Kill Creativity?* Web link: tinyurl.com/qjx6j4v

Simon, B. (1974). *The Two Nations and the Educational Structure 1780–1870*. London: Lawrence & Wishart.

Smith, A. (1776). *The Wealth of Nations*. Web link: tinyurl.com/y5pqrhv2

Watters, A. (2015). *The Invented History of "The Factory Model of Education"*. Web link: tinyurl.com/y8dmn4h8

14

ALEXANDER VON HUMBOLDT

"The man who made nature modern."[1]

Alexander von Humboldt (1769–1859) was a polymath born into a Prussian aristocratic family. He was privately educated in political history, economics, Classics, languages, and mathematics, and then spent a year at Göttingen University in 1789 studying mineralogy and geology.

By 1797, he knew that he wanted to focus on scientific exploration and obtained permission from the Spanish government to visit colonies in Central and South America. Von Humboldt (and French botanist Aimé Bonpland) spent five years there, from 1799 to 1804, covering almost 10,000 kilometres on foot, horseback, and in canoes. They returned with around 60,000 plant specimens and data on longitudes and latitudes, the Earth's magnetic field, daily observations of pressure and temperatures, as well as statistical data on socio-economic conditions in Mexico. Von Humboldt was the first to ascribe mountain sickness to lack of oxygen and studied the current off the west coast of South America which was named after him. On his way back, he visited Thomas Jefferson in Washington,[2] who called him one of the greatest ornaments of the age.[3]

The years 1804 to 1827 were devoted to publication of the South American data in 30 volumes. Of the greatest significance were meteorological data (he invented isotherms and isobars) and pioneering studies on the relationship between geography and flora and fauna, and the conclusions he drew about the role played by volcanic forces in the formation of the Earth's crust.[4] In 1829 he visited Russia and Siberia, making valuable geographical, geological, and meteorological observations in Central Asia.

He began to write his most influential book, *Cosmos: A Sketch of a Physical Description of the Universe*, in 1834 when he was 65.[5] It was unlike any previous book about nature and was an attempt to bring together everything that was known about the heavens and the Earth. This was a collaborative venture with von Humboldt working with a huge range of expert and well-travelled people across the disciplines, all of whom willingly gave of their data and ideas. It was an encyclopaedic venture, and all done by post. The first volume was published in 1845 with its hundred-page introduction setting out von Humboldt's vision of nature as a "wonderful web of organic life".[6] This emphasised the linkages between phenomena rather than seeing them in isolation and promoted a holistic view of nature. It was his greatest contribution to ideas.[7] If nature was a web of life, he said, you needed data on everything from everywhere, and he argued that nature could only be understood by experiencing it. He thought that nature had to be measured and analysed, but also believed that the senses and emotions were crucial aspects of doing this. There was no mention of God in any of it. *Cosmos* proved a bestseller, was widely translated, and very influential across the world.[8]

Von Humboldt had grown up in a world which largely accepted the Cartesian view of a mechanical nature with humans separate from the rest of life. However, he not only presented a radical new vision of nature, but also placed humanity firmly within it. In his *Essay on the Geography of Plants* he stressed the relationships between plants, climate and geography in which their components functioned in relation to each other. In this subjectification of nature, von Humboldt tried to help us to see ourselves as part of the giant web. By accepting this, he believed we might come to see that we had a responsibility to understand nature and nurture it. Web of life is a phrase that we use now when we think of ecosystems, although the term ecology was not coined by von Humboldt, or in his lifetime. Haeckel did so in 1866, some seven years after von Humboldt's death, and it was only in the 1890s that ecology finally emerged as a recognised science. Wulf says that Haeckel was greatly influenced both by von Humboldt – reading *Cosmos* when he was a medical student – and by Darwin – reading *On the Origin of Species* when he worked in Jena. For Haeckel, Darwin's work fell on the fertile ground prepared by von Humboldt and it was in his book *General Morphology of Organisms* that he first used the term ecology (from the Greek *oikos* for household). In doing this, he had given a name to the science first conceived by von Humboldt: a science that explains the inter-relationships and dynamics of life – a science which, inexplicably, is still not properly taught in schools today despite the fact that an understanding of it is essential to knowing our place within the biosphere.[9]

Notes

1 This is the subtitle of an article in the *Los Angeles Times* by Andrea Wulf. See: tinyurl. com/y6hev6hu
2 Von Humboldt was appalled by the toleration of slavery he found in the United States. Wulf quotes him as saying that nature was his teacher and that the greatest lesson was that of freedom.
3 Von Humboldt's travels showed him the extent to which human economic development was destroying the Earth, and he identified three main ways in which humanity was affecting the climate: deforestation (for the growth of monoculture cash crops), extensive irrigation, and uncontrolled emissions into the atmosphere from industry.

4 Over six months in 1827, von Humboldt gave 77 free public lectures (without notes) in Berlin. They were hugely popular, with hundreds attending each talk (half of them women).
5 Four volumes were published during the last 25 years of his life and he was working on the fifth volume when he died aged 90.
6 A second volume appeared in 1847 which explored the internal world of imagination and feelings.
7 For example, von Humboldt was the first to link colonialism to the environmental damage that the exploitation of the land for minerals and cash crops caused.
8 Andrea Wulf says that *Cosmos* awakened American writers and thinkers to the significance of von Humboldt's ideas, and shaped two generations of American scientists, artists, writers and poets. Emerson got an early copy: "The wonderful Humboldt", he said. Poe dedicated his last major work to von Humboldt, and Whitman wrote his book of poems *Leaves of Grass* with *Cosmos* on his desk. Most significantly, as we note elsewhere, Wulf says *Cosmos* was responsible for the maturing of David Henry Thoreau.
9 Haeckel said that ecology was the science of the relationships of an organism with its environment.

Further reading

Farnam Street. (n.d.). *Alexander von Humboldt and the Invention of Nature: Creating a Holistic View of the World Through A Web of Interdisciplinary Knowledge*. Web link: tinyurl.com/y2netuuy

Toomey, D. (n.d.). The Legacy of the Man Who Changed Our View of Nature. *Yale Environment*, 360. Web link: tinyurl.com/y466hd7c

Von Humboldt, A. (1858–1859). *Cosmos: A Sketch of a Physical Description of the Universe*. New York, NY: Harper & Brothers.

Von Humboldt, A. & Bonpland, A. (1807). *Essay on the Geography of Plants*. Berlin: Humboldt State University. Web link: tinyurl.com/y5q45e74

Watson, P. (2010). *The German Genius*. London: Simon & Schuster (177–181).

Wulf, A. (2015). *The Invention of Nature: the adventures of Alexander von Humboldt*. London: John Murray.

15

JOHN CLARE'S ENCLOSURE

"And birds and trees and flowers without a name
All sighed when lawless law's enclosure came."[1]

John Clare (1793–1864) was a poet, an environmentalist, and through his poetry, an environmental educator – although he wouldn't have recognised such modern descriptions.

As the child of a largely illiterate casual labouring family Clare had a limited Dame School education[2] and began to work on the land as a boy. Over time, thanks to a local oral tradition of folk tales and song, and influenced by reading James Thompson's "Seasons",[3] an ability to write verse developed which eventually led, in 1820, to a critically well-received book – *Poems Descriptive of Rural Life and Scenery* – which sold 3,000 copies. Although his poetry ranged over nature, folk literature, social injustice, and the inner self, it is his ability to observe and depict the rich detail and dynamics of the natural world that stands out. But this early writing success faded and his struggles to support his family, combined with a dislocation from his community, took a heavy psychological toll. He spent his last 23 years in a Northampton asylum where he wrote his best work which was mostly published after his death. His poetry only became widely read after the early 1900s.

The Poetry Foundation's entry on Clare[4] quotes R.K.R. Thornton's contribution to the *Dictionary of Literary Biography* which emphasises another aspect of his writing:

"As an observer of what it was like in England in the early nineteenth century, not only for the peasant but also from a peasant point of view, he is irreplaceable," declared Thornton. In Clare's prose, Thornton concluded, "we ... see reflected there in sharp clarity the very essence of a period, a place, a language, a culture, and a time."

Clare was someone who understood our need for a connection to land and place and landscape, and was badly affected by the 1809 Enclosure Act for Helpston (the village where he lived). This granted local landowners permission to divide up and fence-off land, and separate communities from age-old access, excluding the people who had worked, lived and celebrated there. This act of parliament meant that Clare was no longer able to roam at will over the countryside, and his poetry was heavily influenced by the changes. See our chapter on Marx in Nature for further exploration of these developments.

George Monbiot describes the effect of the enclosure act on Clare like this:[5]

> Almost everything Clare loved was torn away. The ancient trees were felled, the scrub and furze were cleared, the rivers were canalised, the marshes drained, the natural curves of the land straightened and squared. Farming became more profitable, but many of the people of Helpston – especially those who depended on the commons for their survival – were deprived of their living. The places in which the people held their ceremonies and celebrated the passing of the seasons were fenced.

Monbiot then added a comment that positions Clare not as an isolated individual rooted in place and time, but as part of a long, global continuum of forced dislocation and alienation:

> What Clare suffered was the fate of indigenous peoples torn from their land and belonging everywhere.

This is, of course, only one view of the enclosures. Another is a tale of improvement: a modernisation of agricultural practices, gains in productivity and an increased ability to feed a growing population, keeping Thomas Malthus's predictions at bay.[6]

England's enclosures began after the Black Death[7] had near-emptied parts of the countryside of people, and land holdings were consolidated and fenced. But it was in the 18th and 19th centuries that acts of parliament were passed enabling this to happen in a more systematic way until it ended in 1869 when egregious attempts to enclose Clapham and Wimbledon Commons in London and the Epsom Downs in Surrey concentrated parliament's mind.

Henry Hobhouse (2005) has made a detailed improvement-productivity argument for enclosure in England. He writes:

> In the period 1660–1860, 2.5 million hectares (6 million acres) were brought into better cultivation by enclosure from common land, scrubland, wasteland, poor timberland, and so forth.

He argues that enclosure (before 1845) was driven by a need to produce more food; that is by population growth. Over that period the population had risen from around 5 million (in 1660) to over 18 million and it was eight techniques which, taken together, made feeding that population possible.[8] Hobhouse argues that the main benefits of enclosure over the previous system of land held in common (a system into which Clare was born) was that it made possible appropriate husbandry, "sensible rotations, manuring, fallow cultivations". It is also obvious that it facilitated family enterprise and investment which made contributions to both the individual and the common good.[9] Such a gimlet-eyed economist's perspective will not be to everyone's taste as it is clear that enclosure led to the forced social dislocation of thousands of people who moved into the towns and cities.

John Clare saw no benefit in the enclosure of Helpston in 1809. His poem, "To a Fallen Elm"[10] draws up the plusses and minuses in what Timothy Ziegenhagen[11] describes as "a complex expression of loss and anger". As such, it seems appropriate to give Clare the last word. This is an extract from "The Mores".[12]

> Far spread the moorey ground a level scene
> Bespread with rush and one eternal green
> That never felt the rage of blundering plough
> Though centurys wreathed spring's blossoms on its brow
> Still meeting plains that stretched them far away
> In uncheckt shadows of green brown, and grey
> Unbounded freedom ruled the wandering scene
> Nor fence of ownership crept in between
> To hide the prospect of the following eye
> Its only bondage was the circling sky
> ...
> These paths are stopt – the rude philistine's thrall
> Is laid upon them and destroyed them all
> Each little tyrant with his little sign
> Shows where man claims earth glows no more divine
> But paths to freedom and to childhood dear
> A board sticks up to notice 'no road here'
> And on the tree with ivy overhung
> The hated sign by vulgar taste is hung
> As tho' the very birds should learn to know
> When they go there they must no further go
> Thus, with the poor, scared freedom bade goodbye
> And much they feel it in the smothered sigh
> And birds and trees and flowers without a name
> All sighed when lawless law's enclosure came
> And dreams of plunder in such rebel schemes
> Have found too truly that they were but dreams.

Notes

1 From John Clare's poem "The Mores": tinyurl.com/y8yejfqe
2 See: tinyurl.com/y7ykpfm7
3 The poem is here: tinyurl.com/y8q26bsg
4 See poetryfoundation.org/poets/john-clare. This provides a brief critical summary of Clare's poetic contribution, mapping this onto his difficult life.
5 The article is here: tinyurl.com/y8juaq4w
6 See Scott and Vare (2018).
7 The Black Death ravaged England in 1348/1349 and 1361/1362, and again in 1665/1666.
8 These were: better tillage, new implements, better ratio between seed sown and seed harvested, suiting crop to soil, crop rotations, manuring, new crops, and the application of all the above to cattle husbandry.
9 Although not always, as Repton notes in *Fragments on the Theory and Practice of Landscape Gardening*: "By cutting down the timber and getting an act to enclose the commons [he] had doubled all the rents. The old mossy and ivy-covered pale was replaced by a new and lofty close paling; not to confine the deer, but to exclude mankind ..."
10 "To a Fallen Elm": allpoetry.com/To-a-Fallen-Elm
11 "Domestic Tree": Freedom and Home in "The Fallen Elm": tinyurl.com/yajbg9lb
12 The poem is here: tinyurl.com/y8yejfqe. The spelling and punctuation are Clare's original.
13 Andrew Motion's review of the book is here: tinyurl.com/ybkxg8oz

Further reading

Bate, J. (2003). *John Clare: a biography*. London: Picador. [13]

BBC. (n.d.). *In Our Time John Clare*. Web link: bbc.co.uk/programmes/b08cstfr

Hobhouse, H. (2005). *Forces of Change: an unorthodox view of history*. New York, NY: Shoemaker & Hoard.

Romantic Circles. (n.d.). A refereed website devoted to the study of Romantic-period literature and culture. Web link: rc.umd.edu

Scott, W. & Vare, P. (2018). *The World We'll Leave Behind*. London: Routledge/Greenleaf.

16

MARX IN NATURE

"Labour and production constitute the active human transformation of nature, but also of human nature, the human relation to nature and human beings themselves."[1]

In a 2018 article for the *International Socialist Review*, Elizabeth Terzakis asks, given that the impacts of climate change are becoming a daily reality for people around the globe, why is it so difficult for governments and their representatives to deal with this issue?

The answer, she says, is a simple one:

while the ruling class can imagine an end to the world, neither they nor many ecologists can imagine an end to capitalism. For this reason, all of their solutions must fall within the bounds of the market system. But the market system, with its need for constant growth and its inability to see the natural world as anything other than an exploitable resource, is in direct and inherent antagonism to the preservation of nature.

There is undoubtedly something in this argument, as far as it goes.[2] Terzakis goes much further, however, and says that there can be no solution to the problem of climate change without an end to capitalism, adding that this is "a fact that becomes very clear when we examine Karl Marx's writings on nature".

What, then, do these say?

In *The Poverty of Philosophy* Marx (1963) wrote that human society rests on the free appropriation of material and resources from nature, and that there can be no human existence without such appropriation. At one level, this is common sense, and it led Marx to a critique of capitalism which intertwined economic and ecological elements. Marx saw that, throughout history, it was through their labour that humans appropriated nature to satisfy their needs. Thus, the interaction of society and nature is a universal and necessary phenomenon.

As the opening quote to this chapter illustrates, as humans interact with nature we not only change it, but are ourselves changed. This has been widely understood for a long time, not least by the Romantic poets, and – in a non-Marxist sense – continues to be the core idea today behind movements arguing that human well-being is enhanced through direct contact with the natural world.

For Marx, humans obviously needed nature (all those biospheric goods and services) in order to live whilst being clearly a part of nature itself ("a single totality" as Terzakis puts it). Human labour, Marx wrote, was a process "by which man, through his own actions, mediates, regulates, and controls the metabolism between himself and nature".[3] He described the process of human labour as a "metabolic exchange"[4] between human beings and nature: that is, between our organic human bodies and our inorganic nature body.[5] In this sense, soil fertility is no longer about the nutritional content of soil, but part of our social relationships. This is a significant departure from the common-sense understanding of our human dependence on the biosphere mentioned above.

Marx then argued that the private acquisition of land through gifting, enclosure and subsequent accumulation (as happened in the Middle Ages in England) created a "metabolic rift" which destroyed our direct relationship with nature. In his *Economic and Philosophic Manuscripts of 1844* he set out his theory of alienation in which he argued that workers become estranged from their humanity and nature through living in capitalist economies.[6] There are four aspects to this. Workers are alienated from:

- the products of their labour as these do not contribute directly to satisfying human needs
- the labouring process; since this is something that makes us human, we are thus alienated from ourselves
- each other, because we now need to compete to survive; as we are by (human) nature social, we are thus alienated from ourselves
- nature – our inorganic body; hence the alienation of humans from their labour is inseparable from the alienation of human beings from nature

In pre-capitalist days, whether communal, feudal or other, social relationships to nature were more directly linked to survival if not to flourishing.[7] Initially, most human relationships with the goods and services that the biosphere provided were largely unmediated and involved gathering, hunting, small-scale growing and rearing, and raiding or other forms of thieving. In post-Norman times in England, when much land was distributed by a king to more or less dutiful barons and knights, the social organisation was mostly feudal with peasant families working land for themselves and paying tithes to the landowner.[8] Here, pasture and forests were often in common use where cattle and sheep could be grazed, rabbits hunted, fungi and berries foraged, wood gathered, etc.[9]

As we note in our chapter on John Clare, England's enclosures began after the Black Death[10] had near-emptied parts of the countryside of people. As a consequence, land holdings were able to be consolidated and fenced. But it was in the 18th century at the time of the Industrial Revolution that acts of parliament began to be passed enabling this to happen in a more systematic way, with much common land being lost as a communal resource. This was a widespread practice.[11]

Marx says that with the rise of capitalism, all this changed, but market-based exchange (which is integral to capitalism) had been in existence long before what we now recognise as industrial development,[12] and as Terzakis notes, the rift between the majority of people and the land began under feudalism, and was completed with capitalist industrialisation. Many people left the land to go into growing urban areas. Those who remained often became agricultural workers earning wages and having to pay rents. By remaining, Marx argued that they became both socially and intellectually isolated, thus lacking opportunities to fully develop as human beings. For those leaving for towns, it was, of course, much worse as we explore in our chapters on development issues in 18th-century England.

Today, we might see limited differences between the two groups; neither had access to anything approaching appropriate education, and life was, in Thomas Hobbes's words, likely to be isolated and "poore, nasty, brutish, and short".[13] Those in the country would, just as now, likely have had better access to clean air.

Marx saw that it was necessary (and possible) to govern human metabolism with nature, but that this was impossible under the social and political (i.e. capitalist) conditions that prevailed at the time. A better future was possible, he said, when socialised humans governed their relationships with nature through collective control, rather than through the dictates of capital and markets. This would not, however, automatically be an outcome of the transition to a socialist economy but would need to be carefully and centrally organised through the rational division of labour and between town and country where soil fertility would be key; just, perhaps, as the prayers of the monks in the great Cistercian monasteries of the Middle Ages were supported in material ways by lay-brothers who ran their farms.[14]

Much of Marx's argumentation on humans and nature, and his idealistic take on what was future possible, relied on the premise that humans and nature were at one with each other before capitalism came along. This, however, is essentially a prelapsarian, Edenic argument with capital taking the place of the serpent. It also depends on human nature being exclusively cooperative and not as it is today (as always): an uneasy clash of the collaborative and the competitive. The best that can be said of this notion is that in Marx's version it's not women who get the blame.[15]

Notes

1 Foster, Clark and York (2010:228).
2 Many would argue that modern regulated market mechanisms, carbon taxes and other incentives (all undreamed of by Marx) offer ways of not only holding exploitation in check but also of promoting ecologically sound development whilst providing financial

discipline and innovative developments. As *The Economist* put it on September 20, 2019: "Market economies are the wells that produce the response climate change requires." See: tinyurl.com/y4ea2b3p

3 Marx (1977:283).

4 There are literal and metaphoric dimensions to Marx's idea of metabolic exchange. Literally, on the ground, it is manifest by humans exploiting the Earth through agriculture and then fertilising the (now slightly depleted) ground with animal waste products (compost, manure, etc.). This has been used for a long time in order to maintain soil fertility and the practice is found today in all organic farming. For an exploration of the other meaning, we refer you to the huge number of works on "metabolic rift", particularly those by John Bellamy Foster.

5 See this link for an explanation of this phrase: tinyurl.com/qnxb8qw

6 See Kristy Simon on Profolus: tinyurl.com/y3jscxfo

7 We have deliberately avoided the idea of subsistence, as many see this as a negative framing by capitalist societies of flourishing pre-capitalist systems. Inupiat Eskimos certainly object to the term.

8 Up to the time of the dissolution of the monasteries by Thomas Cromwell in the 16th century, much land had also been owned, one way or another, by the Church.

9 This permission did not usually extend to deer which were reserved for hunting by upper social groups.

10 The Black Death ravaged England in 1348/1349 and 1361/1362, and again in the mid-1660s.

11 Marx is said to have noted that, in Prussia, some 80% of prosecutions in the early 1840s were the result of wood being taken for personal use from newly private forests.

12 For example, a local town to one of us, Melksham in Wiltshire, was granted a Friday market and a Michaelmas fair in 1219. Many such grants are much older.

13 "No arts; no letters; no society; and which is worst of all, continual fear, and danger of violent death: and the life of man, solitary, poor, nasty, brutish, and short" (Hobbes, *Leviathan*). See: tinyurl.com/y42dp25m

14 These Cistercian farms eventually made their communities very rich through wool exports.

15 We go further into this argument in Chapter 42, Behind the cenes.

Further reading

Foster, J.B. (2000). *Marx's Ecology: Materialism and Nature*. New York, NY: Monthly Review Press.

Foster, J.B. (2013). Marx and the Rift in the Universal Metabolism of Nature. *Monthly Review*, 65 (7). Web link: tinyurl.com/yckw45yp

Foster, J.B., Clark, B. & York, R. (2010). *The Ecological Rift: Capitalism's War on the Earth*. New York, NY: Monthly Review Press.

Marx, K. (1963). *The Poverty of Philosophy*. New York, NY: International Publishers.

Marx, K. (1977). *Capital*, vol. 1. New York, NY: Vintage Books.

Marx, K. & Engels, F. (n.d.). *Collected Works (1835–1895)*. Chadwell Heath: Lawrence & Wishart.

O'Connor, J. (1988). Capitalism, Nature, Socialism: A Theoretical Introduction. *Capitalism, Nature, Socialism*, 1 (1), 11–38.

Piketty, T. (2020). *Capital and Ideology*. Cambridge, MA: Belknap Press.

Polanyi, K. (1967). *The Great Transformation*, Boston, MA: Beacon Press.

Terzakis, E. (2018). Marx and nature: Why we need Marx now more than ever. *International Socialist Review*, 109. Web link: tinyurl.com/y5segulj

17

THOREAU AND *WALDEN*

"Shall I not have intelligence with the earth? Am I not partly leaves and vegetable mould myself?"[1]

Andrea Wulf (2015)[2] argues that it was Alexander von Humboldt's encyclopaedic book, *Cosmos: A Sketch of A Physical Description of the Universe*, that was responsible for the maturing of David Henry Thoreau as an influential writer and thinker; and someone now revered for his philosophical exploration of the human condition in relation to nature, and his view that simplicity, harmony, and beauty might be models for just social and cultural co-existence.[3]

Thoreau was born in 1817 in Concord, Massachusetts. He was the son of a pencil maker and went to Harvard in 1833. Following his return, he ran a progressive school for three years with his brother John. Thoreau met Ralph Waldo Emerson in Concord, who introduced him to local writers and thinkers.[4] Emerson encouraged Thoreau to keep a journal and contribute to a quarterly transcendentalist periodical, *The Dial*, which he and others had set up. In 1842, the first of Thoreau's essays about nature was published.[5]

In 1845, following his brother's death, a troubled Thoreau, acting on a suggestion, built and then lived in a cabin next to Walden Pond in a wood owned by Emerson. He lived there for just over two years, doing so because he wished to live "deliberately, to front only the essential facts of life, and see if I could not learn what it had to teach, ..."[6] It was his intention to live simply, as self-sufficiently as possible, and have time for contemplation, walking, writing, and for being in and with nature.[7] He filled a notebook with reflections on his experiences which eventually became the first draft of his classic book, *Walden*.

It took seven drafts before Thoreau was happy to publish *Walden*, and it was trying to make meaning out of his experience that caused the redrafting. "What is this pond a-doing?", he had written in his journal. "What does it mean?"[8] On leaving the woods, he took up a surveying job and collected specimens for Harvard, all the time keeping his journal and recording what he observed.

Initially, Thoreau had been drawn to transcendentalism. This idealistic system of thinking espoused by Emerson is part of the Romantic movement and is grounded in a belief in the unity of creation and the innate goodness of people. It relies on insight over both logic and experience for the revelation of the deepest truths. However, in 1849, sometime after his time in the woods, and as his empiricism developed, Thoreau increasingly found this way of thinking about nature incompatible, and then irreconcilable, with his view that connections and detail are needed if unity is to be comprehended. He adopted a regular routine of study, journal writing[9] and walking, and a careful compilation of field notes. These were notes of such detail that they are still referenced today. Thoreau also analysed the patterns and cycles he observed, and used experiments and analysis to explain phenomena such as forest regeneration.

Thoreau took up his draft of *Walden* again in 1852 and after much reworking, it was published in 1854 as a series of 18 essays. This was not just a record of his experiment in simple living, but also an exploration of work, leisure, self-reliance and individualism. Von Humboldt is mentioned regularly in his journal writing[10] and *Walden* was his personal response to *Cosmos*. It was, says Wulf, the interconnected view of nature expressed in *Cosmos* that gave Thoreau the confidence to weave his poetic imagination with science in a novel way, bringing together parts with the whole, and fact with wonder and imagination. But his mind, Wulf says, had been ready.

Thoreau's nature writings were not immediately successful or influential, or always positively received. He paid to have his first book[11] printed which landed him with a large debt (and unsold books), and *Walden* sold a disappointing 2,000 copies in five years. And yet the elegantly written *Walden* is now a classic of environmental writing and American literature more widely, and Thoreau is viewed as a cultural icon. He established the tradition of nature writing in the United States, but it is for his frank posing of wide-ranging questions about how the American society was developing economically (a rapid, careless expansion), environmentally (the misuse of nature and destruction of ecosystems and habitats), and democratically (a despicable slave-dependent state) that we should perhaps remember him. In this reading of his life, his focus was with wider sustainability issues rather than narrow environmental ones. He was well before his time in addressing the problems that we are causing by how we live, although the attractions of living a simple life probably seem as unattractive to most people today as they did then.

Notes

1 This is one of a number of memorable quotes from *Walden*. It comes from the "Solitude" essay.
2 Wulf's (2015) chapter 19 ("Poetry, Science and Nature") is a long examination of Thoreau's life and the influence of von Humboldt upon it.

3 Like von Humboldt, Thoreau was passionately against slavery and was an active abolitionist participating in the Underground Railroad and attacking what he saw the morally
bankrupt Fugitive Slave Law. He supported John Brown, the abolitionist militia leader.
He also took part in civil disobedience, refusing to pay local taxes whose purpose he
disapproved of. His 1849 essay *On the Duty of Civil Disobedience (Resistance to Civil Government)* was probably just as influential as *Walden*, but on a different audience.

4 Emerson was a Unitarian minister who eventually found its beliefs too limiting for his
thinking. His *Essays* (1841–1844), *Representative Men* (1850), and *English Traits* (1856) set
out his beliefs. Watson (2010:177) says that Emerson described von Humboldt as "one
of the wonders of the world, like Aristotle, like Julius Caesar … who appears from time
to time as if to show us the possibilities of the human mind".

5 *Natural History of Massachusetts.*

6 The quote is from *Walden*, chapter 2.

7 Thoreau did not spend all the two years in the woods, returning regularly to Concord to
visit his family and others, and even went on a trip to Maine.

8 Quoted by Wulf (2017:255).

9 Wulf (2017) quotes Thoreau wondering whether anything he ever wrote could be
better than his journal, and to Wulf the answer is clearly no. She writes: "Thoreau's love
for nature sings off his journal pages in spring. His winter writing slices right into the
heart. His entries, day after day, are testimony to the power of renewal and rebirth – and
to the importance of harnessing the human sense of wonder to better understand and
protect the Earth. In our age of the Anthropocene, as we distance ourselves from the
cyclical rhythms of nature, we are disconnecting from our planet. Thoreau's journal is a
reminder of what is at stake."

10 "This habit of close observation, – in Humboldt, Darwin, and others. Is it to be kept up
long, this science?" Thoreau asks in an entry from July 1851.

11 *A Week on the Concord and Merrimack Rivers.*

12 The texts of *Walden* and *On the Duty of Civil Disobedience* can be read here: tinyurl.com/
y7sojb62

Further reading

Emerson, R.W. (1836/1985). *Nature*. Boston, MA: Beacon Press.

Thoreau, D.H. (1854). *Walden; or, Life in the Woods*. Boston, MA: Ticknor and Fields.[12]

Von Humboldt, A. (1858–1859). *Cosmos: A Sketch of a Physical Description of the Universe*.
New York, NY: Harper & Brothers.

Walden Woods Project. (n.d.). *The Journal of Henry David Thoreau*. Web link: walden.org/
collection/journals

Walls, L.D. (2018). *Henry David Thoreau: A Life*. Chicago, IL: University of Chicago Press.

Watson, P. (2010). *The German Genius*. London: Simon & Schuster (177–181).

Wulf, A. (2015). *The Invention of Nature: the adventures of Alexander von Humboldt*. London:
John Murray.

Wulf, A. (2017). Walden Wasn't Thoreau's Masterpiece. *The Atlantic*, November. Web link:
tinyurl.com/y8kva3fa

18

THE SIGNIFICANCE OF JOHN MUIR

"Wildness was ever sounding in our ears, and Nature saw to it that besides school lessons and church lessons some of her own lessons should be learned, perhaps with a view to the time when we should be called to wander in wildness to our heart's content."[1]

John Muir (1838–1914) was an explorer, mountaineer, conservationist, botanist, amateur geologist and a writer of distinction. It is probable that there was no more influential figure in the United States when it comes to the preservation of wilderness, at least when accomplishments are considered. Muir's passion for wild nature led to his activism, and his writings helped people understand the importance of the wild to both the biosphere and to humanity. Muir laid the groundwork that helped to create the world's first national park system.[2]

Muir was born in Scotland and was eleven when he emigrated with his family to the USA. In his childhood, he grew to love the wild places around the coastal town of Dunbar, in East Lothian near Edinburgh. It's clear from his own account for the Sierra Club[3] that the young Muir was a restless spirit who rebelled against a strict upbringing. This autobiographical account is full of fist fights with local youth resulting in thrashings by father and teacher alike. Muir's love of the East Lothian landscape meant that he wandered at will along the coast and in the countryside.

Seeing all his later activism and adventures set out in detail, as the Sierra Club does,[4] is to get a picture of a man waging a long campaign. Muir popularised spending time in wild areas as a source of recreation, enjoyment, solace and fulfilment. He was a preservationist whose writing about his travels and about wild areas and life were read by millions[5] and his lasting effects on the United States are numerous. His approach was that of a guerrilla fighter rather than a general with brigades and regiments under arms. It's as though, in adulthood, his childhood fighting took on another form; not against youth this time, but against indifference, cynicism, exploitation, business and special interests, where the weapons of choice were not fists but publicity, writing and persuasion. It was long drawn-out with skirmishes, running battles, stands-off, truces, and defeats; as well as victories to be savoured. But the battle was never won as it never will be. No matter how much treasure was saved it remains vulnerable as recent changes in the USA following the election of President Trump have illustrated once again.[6]

While we understand that Muir studied Wordsworth in his youth and even visited his grave on a return to Europe in later life,[7] it is not possible to know whether Muir knew Wordsworth's 1802 poem My Heart Leaps up, or if he studied it at school. It might seem unlikely that English romantic poets were part of the curriculum in Dunbar in the 1840s, progressive though Scottish education was at that time. It is more certain, however, that the sentiments of the poem would have been felt and even expressed by Muir at some point in his life.

> My heart leaps up when I behold
> A rainbow in the sky:
> So was it when my life began;
> So is it now I am a man;
> So be it when I shall grow old,
> Or let me die!
> The Child is father of the Man;
> And I could wish my days to be
> Bound each to each by natural piety.[8]

If the rainbow represents the natural world more generally and the poem records the lasting impact of nature on someone who "bring(s) … a heart that watches and receives" as another Wordsworth poem, The Tables Turned,[9] has it, then this is just, according to his own account, what happened to Muir as he grew up.

After his eight years of formal schooling in Scotland (elementary school from the age of 3 and then grammar school from age 8), there was none on offer in the US and he had to educate himself. It wasn't until 1861 when he was 23 that Muir had any instruction in botany.[10] But this exposure to it was a significant (life) experience, and he became impassioned. He took his first botanical expedition along the Wisconsin River to the Mississippi in 1863.

Influence, however, is a two-way street, and it is also the case that, like many writers and thinkers in North America, Muir owed an intellectual debt of gratitude to the 19th century Prussian polymath, Alexander von Humboldt whom we write about elsewhere. Andrea Wulf (2015) says that it was von Humboldt who inspired Muir's ecological thinking. "How intensely I desire to be a Humboldt," Muir declared when he was in his 20s.[11] Wulf adds that the Muir quote "When we try to pick out anything by itself, we find it hitched to everything else in the universe"[12] obviously acknowledges von Humboldt's idea that everything is connected.[13]

Five particular experiences might be thought to have had a particular influence on Muir: his childhood in East Lothian,[14] emigration, his mentoring by Wisconsin botanist Jeanne Carr, the botanic influence of Milton Griswold, and the writings of von Humboldt, with his childhood experiences creating a foundation for what followed. A key question has to be whether anyone other than Muir would have been similarly influenced and turned out as he did, having had the same experiences and encounters.

The answer seems clear, as no one did. None of the young lads who roamed the East Lothian beaches in the 1840s turned out as John Muir did, even if some also emigrated to the USA. Nor did everyone that Milton Griswold explained botany to in the 1860s, whether beneath a black locust tree or not. This suggests that experiences are not indiscriminate in their influence. That is, although they might have an effect which may never be lost, it does not follow because the person having an experience is as important as the experience itself, if not more so.

We explore these important questions in Chapter 32, on the work of Thomas Tanner in the late 1970s which grew into what became known as significant life experience research during the 1980s and 1990s.

Notes

1 See note 14 for a fuller quote.
2 Muir had nothing to do with the Yosemite Act of 1864 which protected the Yosemite Valley from settlement and gave it to California as a State Park. But he did influence Yosemite becoming a National Park in 1890.
3 John Muir was the founder of the Sierra Club in 1892. Its website has a John Muir Exhibit that explores his life and his contribution to conservation in the USA. See: vault. sierraclub.org/john_muir_exhibit
4 The Sierra Club timeline is here: tinyurl.com/y5kaphko
5 Muir's direct activism helped to save the Yosemite Valley and other areas. His vision of nature's value for its own sake and for its spiritual benefits to humanity helped to change the way we look at the natural world.
6 Here's the *National Geographic*'s running list of how President Trump is changing environmental policy: tinyurl.com/y3ka4n8l
7 Muir's debt to Wordsworth is mentioned by Jonathan Bate in his 2020 book *Radical Wordsworth: The Poet Who Changed the World*, published by William Collins.
8 The Wordsworth poem is here: poets.org/poem/my-heart-leaps
9 "The Tables Turned". See: tinyurl.com/y6xcywmo
10 The Sierra Club says that this was from Milton Griswold, a classmate, and it took place beneath a black locust tree near the student residence hall where he was then living.
11 John Muir in his late twenties, writing to his mentor Jeanne Carr, the Wisconsin botanist, quoted in Wulf (2015). Von Humboldt is not mentioned in the Sierra Club timeline.
12 Quoted here: discoverjohnmuir.com
13 Muir left behind heavily annotated copies of von Humboldt's books.
14 This includes walks in the countryside with his grandfather which, Muir said, were his "earliest recollections". He added: "But no punishment, however sure and severe, was of any avail against the attraction of the fields and woods. It had other uses, developing memory, etc., but in keeping us at home it was of no use at all. Wildness was ever sounding in our ears, and Nature saw to it that besides school lessons and church lessons some of her own lessons should be learned, perhaps with a view to the time when we should be called to wander in wildness to our heart's content. ... These were my first excursions, – the beginnings of lifelong wanderings" (Muir n.d.).

Further reading

Muir, J. (n.d.). The Story of My Boyhood and Youth; chapter 1: a boyhood in Scotland. *Sierra Club*. Web link: tinyurl.com/y3srxyvv

Tanner, T. (1980). Significant Life Experiences: A New Research Area in Environmental Education. *Journal of Environmental Education*, 11 (4), 20–24.

Toomey, D. (n.d.). The Legacy of the Man Who Changed Our View of Nature. *Yale Environment*, 360. Web link: tinyurl.com/y466hd7c

Wulf, A. (2015). *The Invention of Nature: the adventures of Alexander von Humboldt*. London: John Murray.

19

FRILUFTSLIV

"Nature is the home of culture – friluftsliv is a way home."[1]

Friluftsliv is a Norwegian word that can be rendered simply in English as fresh –
air – living.[2] It is, however, one of those complex cultural notions that do not
translate easily into other languages: rather like the German idea of bildung. It is
said to have first been used in print by Ibsen in his 1859 poem "On the Heights",
in which the main character chooses a life in wild nature away from the settlement
where he grew up.[3]

There is certainly more to friluftsliv than this literal translation suggests. It is not
just about going for the occasional walk, taking a lunchtime break in the fresh air,
or a spot of gardening at the weekend, as this extract from an essay about Ibsen and
the idea sets out:

> Henrik Ibsen's meaning with "Friluftsliv" might best be interpreted as the
> total appreciation of the experience one has when communing with the
> natural environment, not for sport or play, but for its value in the develop-
> ment of one's entire spiritual and physical being. At its heart is the full
> identification and fulfilment of body and soul one experiences when
> immersed in nature.[4]

Friluftsliv concerns identity, and its origins cannot be separated from the struggles
of the Norwegian people to be free of political dominance by Swedes and Danes.
As originally conceived, friluftsliv was seen as a product of European Romanticism
and as a movement against the Enlightenment. This was led by artists and philosophers protesting against Descartes's reduction of nature into *res extensa*: something
which had dimensions but no intrinsic value. In their view, nature, as well as
humans, had intrinsic value.

In their summary of the genesis of the idea of friluftsliv, Faarlund, Dahle and Jensen (2007) say that its essence is a personal encounter with nature; its antithesis is experiences that are commercialised or competitive. Charlotte Workman argues that "friluftsliv does not mean abandoning modern day life and technology; rather, it is simply embodied by spending more time in nature. Learning to fish, going for walks and climbing trees might all be paths to nature, but genuine friluftsliv is about being present in nature and becoming part of it".[5] Going further, Hans Gelter (2000) argues that it's about you getting into nature, and about getting nature into you.[6]

Gelter's comments highlight a sharp distinction between the core idea of friluftsliv and so much mainstream outdoor activity and learning today where the point is to do something: for example, to achieve goals, to develop skills, to learn facts, to improve mental health, to get stronger or fitter. None of these are ignoble purposes, but friluftsliv rests on a simpler premise: just to be and to reconnect with the natural world in the mutual ways outlined at the end of the previous paragraph.

Rather inevitably, however, over time the term friluftsliv has evolved from its original meaning and come to mean being outdoors and purposefully active, with magazines and websites now devoted to it – not only in Scandinavia but farther afield.[7] It is now described as a lifestyle trend on a par with Hygge by magazines such as *Country Living*,[8] and the BBC says that in Sweden, "a country of 10 million people, there are 25 non-profit associations anchored to *friluftsliv*, with 1.7 million memberships spread across 9,000 local and regional clubs".[9]

It's certainly possible to see friluftsliv as a sort of curriculum-free environmental education and it is a long way from most of the outdoor education we are now familiar with as this tends to have specific learning goals, clear-ish outcomes, and grand purposes. Friluftsliv might not be about how people see most teaching and lecturing but it involves, as Gelter puts it, "learning the ways of yourself and your place in the more-than-human world, and learning the ways of every creature and phenomenon you meet on your journey through life". Although outdoor education is on the curriculum in most Scandinavian schools, as with most children's experience of forest schools, its goals are more prosaic and instrumental than the deeper philosophical ideas embedded in friluftsliv.

Gelter says that as humans evolved in a world of fractal structures (waves, mountains, fire, living with seasonal, daily and biological rhythms), the nature and value of these were slowly encoded within our make-up. But in our fast, increasingly digital world, we don't have to rely on these as much as we did and can be even largely unaware of them. This disharmony, as Gelter terms it, leads to stress, fatigue and low self-esteem. Hence, friluftsliv is about opening our senses and returning once again to be more in tune with nature and becoming interconnected – this assumes or hopes that humanity's future lies in returning to a former relationship with nature rather than adapting to a radically different, technologically mediated existence.

Although some will find this rather New Age and best experienced in places like Glastonbury, there is little to be lost and much to be gained by spending time in the open air with an open mind and sensing what happens. In essence, it's little different from what Wordsworth suggested over 200 years ago.

Notes

1 The title of a paper by Faarlund, Dahle and Jensen given at the eighth World Wilderness Congress symposium. See: tinyurl.com/y4nmma22. The simple idea here is that returning to nature, is returning home.
2 Dictionaries translate the Norwegian "fri" as clear, but Geoffrey Guy translates the term as fresh-air living which makes better English sense; see: tinyurl.com/yxobmeyd
3 Ibsen's use of friluftsliv is here: tinyurl.com/yyejkqzj
4 Quoted in "Henrik Ibsen's use of 'friluftsliv'", by Dag T. Elgvin: tinyurl.com/yyejkqzj
5 Workman's video *Finding Friluftsliv // a documentary* is at: vimeo.com/64425721
6 In much contemporary outdoor education there is much emphasis on the first part of this, but not the second.
7 See for example: tinyurl.com/yy2gmh7k and friluftsliv.no
8 See: tinyurl.com/y3xt9xqz
9 See: tinyurl.com/y4u98soe

Further reading

Faarlund, N., Dahle, B. & Jensen, A. (2007). Nature is the Home of Culture – Friluftsliv is a Way Home. In A. Watson, J. Sproull & L. Dean (Eds.), *Science and stewardship to protect and sustain wilderness values: Eighth World Wilderness Congress symposium. Proceedings RMRS-P-49.* Fort Collins, CO: US Department of Agriculture, Forest Service, Rocky Mountain Research Station. Web link: tinyurl.com/y4nmma22

Gelter, H. (2000). Friluftsliv: The Scandinavian Philosophy of Outdoor Life. *Canadian Journal of Environmental Education*, 5, 77–94.

Pedersen-Gurholt, K. (2008). Norwegian friluftsliv and ideals of becoming an "educated man". *Journal of Adventure Education and Outdoor Learning*, 8 (1), 55–70.

Reed, P. & Rothenberg, D. (Eds). (1993). *Wisdom in the open air: The Norwegian roots of deep ecology.* Minneapolis, MN: University of Minnesota Press.

Wilson, J. (1988). *The history and traditions of Friluftsliv.* Dissertation at the University of Newcastle upon Tyne.

20

PATRICK GEDDES

"Care of Mother Earth is the prime task of man."[1]

Patrick Geddes (1854–1932) was a biologist, environmental educator, sociologist and town planner. He was the first thinker to connect the quality of the environment closely with the quality of education, and was described in the UK documentation presented at the 1977 intergovernmental Tbilisi conference as the "father of environmental education".[2]

Geddes had an unconventional home schooling where the outdoors and nature got more emphasis than books, and it was no surprise when he went to Edinburgh University in 1874 to study botany. He left after a week, however, when he found out that the course completely ignored evolution. He then studied under Huxley in London and got to know Darwin and Wallace when they all were at University College. Although he lectured in zoology at Edinburgh from 1880 to 1888 and held a personal chair of botany at Dundee to 1919, Geddes came to think of himself as a sociologist, and was a professor of sociology in Bombay until 1924, when he moved to France, setting up an urban studies centre and founding Scots College in Montpellier, where he died.

Geddes was heavily influenced by the emerging sense of environmental concern in the 19th century that we associate with Wordsworth, Ruskin, Morris and Spencer. This was a society slowly coming to terms with the socio-economic changes (and environmental and ecological[3] damage)[4] wrought by the Industrial Revolution, and still reeling from the implications of Darwinian thinking that all life had emerged through environmental natural selection.

The rapid growth of urban areas at this time was caused by a range of factors (for example, the enclosure acts)[5] and this intensified poor housing, overcrowding, poverty, wretchedness and disease. The French sociologist Frédéric Le Play, who used surveys and ideas around place, family, community and work for social analysis, influenced Geddes's thinking about such urban social problems; as did Ruskin's view that social processes and urban architecture, organisation and form are related and that, by changing the latter, it was possible to change social structures for the better. Another influence on Geddes was Ebenezer Howard's garden city movement which looked to build utopian cities in which people could live harmoniously together with nature.[6] Geddes came to see that stable and healthy family homes were necessary for the psychological and moral development of the young if they were to be able to have fulfilling lives and make positive social contributions. For him, a key priority was to bring about social development for the benefit of the whole of society. He saw education as a means of urban renewal to create beautiful and functional shared spaces in which all could live. And, because Geddes's citizens had to be able to identify positive change wherever this took place, it implied an education that connected the many branches of human understanding – an approach we'd term holistic today.

But Geddes was unhappy with the education that he saw around him. Whether this was the narrow instrumental curriculum and stultifying pedagogy of the elementary schools which Dickens satirised in *Hard Times*, or the equally (but differently) narrow experience of the public schools, the result was much the same in relation to the lack of human creativity and a waste of potential. He was also scathing about the teaching style of Scottish higher education with its prime focus on exam preparation (as opposed to learning), and he compared it unfavourably with innovations in Germany, and even in England.

When living in Edinburgh, Geddes dedicated himself to urban regeneration through connecting the environment and education. This is why he is widely regarded as an early environmental educator and, 80 years on, in the 1970s became an inspiration for the UK's urban studies movement.[7] Geddes favoured a hands, heart and head approach to learning, and argued that children in contact with their environment would not only learn more effectively but also develop positive attitudes towards it. A hundred years on, such arguments are still having to be made to policy makers.

Whilst in Edinburgh, Geddes also developed extension classes and summer schools through which he tried to put his educational philosophy into practice. Although the schools never attracted huge numbers, they had a positive international reputation. The two main objectives were bringing human understanding together, and promoting a rounded, participative and collaborative approach. The schools emphasised the role of experience in effective learning and, although there were lectures, there were also seminars, demonstrations, fieldwork, and out-of-class experiences more generally.

The first school, in 1885, provided a small number of elementary teachers with practical natural science classes, and the schools developed to provide advanced classes in botany. In 1889 there was the first course in social science. Most of the activities took place in Edinburgh, making use of buildings Geddes had himself renovated. The schools provided direct connections between education, citizenship and social development by discussing with the students the contemporary issues that they saw around them and which were part of their lives.

In 1892, to allow the general public an opportunity to observe people-place relationships, Geddes opened his Outlook Tower in Edinburgh's Old Town.[8] Whilst some termed this a sociological laboratory, it was also clearly an urban environmental studies centre. The Tower's roof gallery had a camera obscura at the top through which the city could be viewed whilst the lower floors had exhibitions about Scotland, empire, and Europe and the world. He used the tower to show how the many branches of human understanding could be drawn together to explain the evolution and nature of human society, and pioneered the use of surveys ("civic surveys for civic service"),[9] bringing together the geology, geography, history, climate, sociology, art, and the economy of Edinburgh, with the community's social institutions. His early work surveying Edinburgh became a model for later developments and led to his being seen as a founder of the British town planning movement.

Geddes was an environmentalist long before the word became fashionable and he taught outdoors wherever possible, going with his students on long walks. His teachings are widely seen to be as relevant today as they were 130 years ago: perhaps even more as the globe's still growing population becomes increasingly urban. Geddes's idea that we can (and if we can we must) learn how to live well in the world by looking critically at how we do live now in relation to our environment, has an appeal when that environment is under greater pressure than ever.

Notes

1 Quoted by Jo Woolf, Writer in Residence at the Royal Scottish Geographical Society: tinyurl.com/wqmpp8c
2 Department of Education and Science/Central Office of Information. (1977). *Environmental education in the UK* 77.
3 Haeckel coined the term *ecology* in the 1860s, setting out a definition in 1866 in a book on morphology.
4 This is part of James Thomson's description of urban life in *The City of Dreadful Night* (1874): "That City's atmosphere is dark and dense, / Although not many exiles wander there, / With many a potent evil influence, / Each adding poison to the poisoned air."
5 Details of the enclosures are here: tinyurl.com/yaebchxr
6 The Garden Cities Association morphed into the Town and Country Planning Association.
7 Ward (1978).
8 See: dundee.ac.uk/geddesinstitute/outlooktower
9 The Civic Survey of Edinburgh (1911), archive.org/details/civicsurveyofedi00gedduoft

Further reading

Geddes, P. (1904). *Civics*: a paper read before the Sociological Society at a meeting in the School of Economics and Political Science (London University) on July 18. Web link: gutenberg.org/files/13205/13205-h/13205-h.htm
Geddes, P. (1915). *Cities in Evolution*. London: Williams and Norgate.

Higgins, P. & Nicol, R. (2010). Sir Patrick Geddes: "Vivendo Discimus" – By Living We Learn. In T.E. Smith & C.E. Knapp (Eds.), *Sourcebook of Experiential Education Key Thinkers and Their Contributions*. London: Routledge.

Ward, C. (1973). *Streetwork: the exploding school*. London: Routledge & Kegan Paul.

Ward, C. (1978). *The Child in the City*. The Anarchist Library. Web link: theanarchistlibrary.org/library/colin-ward-the-child-in-the-city

21

JOHN DEWEY AND THE ECOLOGY OF LEARNING

"The words of John Dewey ought to be banned from all teacher-training institutions."[1]

As it happens, the prolific and long-lived American educationalist and philosopher, John Dewey (1859–1952), never mentioned environmental education; that term only achieved international recognition some years after his death. Environmental education, however, owes much to John Dewey.

For Dewey, education was not a matter of learning dry facts from books, rather it was a process of nurturing and forming individuals *in relation to* society, culture and the wider environment. By learning about their world in this way, learners would become agents in building it anew. This reflects more recent complexity thinking, particularly autopoiesis, which is the idea that we all contribute in creating our world, whether we like it or not. In order to cultivate this sense of agency, Dewey felt that education had to engage the learner in direct experience of the real world. As early as 1897 he wrote:

> the school must represent present life – life as real and vital to the child as that which he carries on in the home, in the neighbourhood, or on the playground. (Dewey 1897:79)

This view pre-empts that of Arthur Lucas in that education is seen as something that should not simply be *about* the world but it should take place *in* it and *for* it.

Dewey's *My Educational Creed* informed what would perhaps be his most significant work of educational thought, *Democracy and Education*, published in 1916. In this Dewey highlighted education's potential for social reconstruction; it was a means by which society would learn to do better. This represents a radical departure from the prevailing conservative view that saw education as a means of achieving cultural continuity. It earned him the reputation of being a progressive, a label that Dewey himself rejected. After all, he valued scientific endeavour and hard-won knowledge, believing that decisions about society's future should be based on evidence. He understood the value of theoretical understanding to those who had learned their way into a discipline but recognised that knowledge first had to relate to the lives of learners. He also emphasised the importance of critical thought so that students would be able to think and learn beyond their classroom teaching.

For Dewey, education had no agenda beyond itself, its own end was simply "one of continual reorganizing, reconstructing, transforming" (1916:68). It was up to parents, politicians, teachers and others to determine the purpose of education. For Dewey, this was obvious: it was the improvement of society. As he observed, a bank robber becoming increasingly skilled at robbing banks was being educated but not in a way likely to improve society. This was not education's fault but the mis-purpose to which it was being put. So, while education (we would probably say "learning") has no end in itself, the *act* of educating is never neutral. Today, those who call for schools, colleges and universities to contribute to building a more sustainable world, are reflecting education in the Deweyan mould.

When Dewey talked of environment he meant it in a broad sense. A teacher's role was to provide students with meaningful interactions with their social and cultural as well as physical environment. That said, he did highlight the importance of nature study, claiming that, while it should be considered part of earth sciences, it was worthy of special attention. This was because of the way that nature had been reduced to the study of components, such as parts of a flower, based in the classroom away from its habitat. It was clear to Dewey that this would deaden the subject for any child and he suggested:

> The real remedy is to make nature study a study of nature, not of fragments made meaningless through complete removal from the situations in which they are produced and in which they operate. (Dewey 1916:280)

Dewey saw that natural objects made impressions on people, therefore educators should use nature to impress the mind. Like Rousseau, Pestalozzi and Froebel before him, he recognised that we are naturally curious about our world and that this should be the foundation of learning: facts in their context, rather than a disjointed, externally imposed curriculum. He saw the fallacy of the Cartesian divide between mind and body, and decried our tendency to deny the inter-relatedness of things; to him it was clear that humans move and thrive within a connected world. There is a direct line from here to environmental education and outdoor learning that focuses on relationships and interdependence within the environment and invites students to participate in outdoor activities as part of their learning experience.

Writing in *Experience and Education* (1938), Dewey reiterated his belief that knowledge, in terms of facts learned from books, only becomes meaningful, i.e. truly internalised, when applied in a real-world context. He advocated that education be based on the quality of experience, although certain parameters should be met for experience to be educative. Firstly, there had to be continuity; experiences come from, and lead to, other experiences, thus driving us on to learn more. The other criterion is interaction; experiences have to meet, or interact with, the needs or goals of a person. Here lies the root of subsequent calls for relevance in education.

This idea of continuity between school-based learning and the rest of the world is an enduring theme in Dewey's work. Later in life he became more keenly aware of what he saw as the transactional whole of all human acts. Writing with fellow transactionalist, Arthur Bentley, in *Knowing and the Known* (1949), he emphasised the inseparability of organisms from their environment, explaining how everything we do, including learning, is part of an ecological whole.

Looking across Dewey's wide range of interests, an overriding concern was democracy. The centrality of education in all this may well have stemmed from the fact that (a) he saw a well-informed populace as an essential component of a democratic state, and (b) his first job was that of school teacher, a role to which he soon decided he was not well suited but which clearly fascinated him thereafter. Dewey exhibits his democratic credentials in the way that he avoids the tendency of philosophers to contemplate life through abstractions, as if philosophy stands aloof from the hard work of everyday life. Instead he believed that abstract ideas had to be understood in terms of their practical effects. This reflects his pragmatist philosophy – yet another strand of Dewey's thought but one we do not have space to examine here. For Dewey, the meaning of something resides in its impact on the world, meanwhile the positive effects of both mind work and physical labour should be shared as widely as possible.

To this day many forms of learning draw on Dewey's notion of education with its combination of experience and reflection. His work does, however, stand in opposition to those who characterise education as teaching "the best which has been thought and said"[2] as if the transmission of culture is education's primary role. Little wonder, then, that some of those with more conservative views about this would prefer that Dewey had written nothing.

Notes

1 A quotation from Chris Woodhead, then Chief Inspector for Schools, writing in the *Daily Telegraph*, April 25, 1999. In the article, entitled "Millennium reputations", Woodhead expressed concern that teachers seemed to see didactic teaching as "outmoded and ineffective".

2 This oft-quoted phrase comes from Matthew Arnold's *Culture and Anarchy* (1869). Arnold was actually defining culture, which he saw as an ever-changing stream, rather than defining a syllabus that we need to teach our children, as is often stated by educational conservatives.

Further reading

Dewey, J. (1897). My Educational Creed. *The School Journal*, LIV (3), 77–80.
Dewey, J. (1916). *Democracy and Education*. Project Gutenberg eBook. Web link: gutenberg. org
Dewey, J. (1938). *Experience and Education*. New York, NY: Simon and Schuster (20).
Dewey, J. & Bentley, A.F. (1949). *Knowing and the Known*. Boston, MS: Beacon Press.

22

BLUT UND BODEN

"Do not rejoice in his defeat, you men. For though the world has stood up and stopped the bastard, the bitch that bore him is in heat again."[1]

Blut und Boden (Blood and Soil) was a late 19th-century social movement in Germany which celebrated the relationship of a people to the land they lived on and cultivated. It stressed the virtues of rural life and was influenced by the Völkisch movement which had its origins in German Romantic Nationalism,[2] which was deeply connected to German culture, history, folklore, and paganism. In time, the Völkisch movement influenced the rise of National Socialism as an ideology, and the Nazi party (NSDAP) as a political force. In this sense, Blut und Boden might equally well be translated as Race and Fatherland.

Peasant farmers were idealised by Nazi ideologues as they were seen to represent the core of racial purity and, literally, to be the bedrock of the economy. In particular, it was Richard Walther Darré[3] who promoted and popularised blood and soil ideology to urge a return to an agrarian economy and a shift away from economic dependence on industry and business which had, from his anti–Semitic perspective, been utterly corrupted by Jews.

In elections before they came to power, the NSDAP had strong support from farm owners who faced debt and the threat of bankruptcy. They were receptive to National Socialist propaganda that said that the traditional basis of rural life was being threatened by the market economy (which, it argued, was controlled by Jews and capitalists), and also by industrialisation and urbanisation. The bargain offered was that farmers would benefit from state protection through their support because they stood at the core of racial superiority and economic stability.

Very soon after coming to power, the Nazis passed the German Hereditary Farm Law[4] with its stipulation that farms could only be inherited by Germans who were able to prove that they had no Jewish or similar non-Aryan ancestors since January 1, 1800. A key aim of this was to preserve the farming community as the "blood-source of the German people".[5] The Law was also a first step towards National Socialist control of the agrarian economy. Here, the aim was to build self-sufficiency in agriculture.

As Reich Farm Leader and Minister of Nutrition and Agriculture, Darré pursued this goal through the Reich Food Estate. This oversaw National Socialist coordination and planning of German agriculture and regulated production, distribution and consumption of agricultural products.[6]

It came to nought, however, as although Hitler shared the blood and soil philosophy, his political priority was rapid industrial expansion to allow re-armament and a preparation for war. It is a great irony that the Farm Law was one of the foundations of the idea of Lebensraum – living space – which envisaged massive settlement projects for farmers in conquered countries to the east as the basis for future German agricultural production. However, the industrialisation needed to prepare for Lebensraum destroyed many German farms rather than boost farming, as great areas of farmland were transformed into roads, airports, and military estates. For example, the building of Germany's Westwall fortifications (the Siegfried Line) between 1936 and 1939 destroyed over 5,000 productive farms. Between 1933 and 1939, the number of farm workers fell from 1.8 to 1.4 million. As a result of these and other policies, there was strict food rationing during the 1930s.[7] By the beginning of the war, Darré's vision had vanished.

Sadly, the slogan Blut und Boden did not die with Darré. Racist North American organisations have adopted it recently and it came to public attention during the 2017 Unite the Right rally in Charlottesville, Virginia[8] and the 2017 White Lives Matter rally in Shelbyville, Tennessee.[9] Happily, there is little prospect of such organisations coming to power in the USA. Whether that can safely be said of far-right groups in Germany and Austria that seem intent on re-writing the history of the Second World War is a more open question.

Notes

1 This quotation comes from a 1941 play by Bertolt Brecht. It tells the story of the rise of Arturo Ui, a fictional 1930s Mob boss in Chicago. The play is a parable on the rise of Hitler and the coming to power of the Nazi Party in Germany.

2 And the efforts to create Germany as a single country.

3 Darré was an influential race theorist who helped the Nazis gain support among Germans living in rural areas. His influential 1933 book, *Neuadel aus Blut und Boden* (A New Aristocracy Based on Blood and Soil) put forward a systemic eugenics programme as a way of addressing all the problems facing the state.

4 September 29, 1933; see: the Holocaust Encyclopedia: tinyurl.com/yyuvpzyf and also German History in Documents and Images (GHDI): tinyurl.com/yylnke64

5 Sources: International Guide to Expert Sources & Media Spokespersons; see: tinyurl.com/y6rfyn98

6 There were complex protocols governing inheritance of the farms; see details here: tinyurl.com/yybtnj5y

7 By 1939 Germany was self-sufficient in bread, potatoes, sugar, meat, and other foodstuffs, but only through rationing. At least 15% of food was still being imported. See: tinyurl.com/y6gug2yz
8 See the CNN report: tinyurl.com/y5byfb68
9 See the CBS News report: tinyurl.com/y4zh7p4e

Further reading

Brecht, B. (2009). *The Resistible Rise of Arturo Ui; a parable play*. London: Bloomsbury.

23

THIS LAND IS YOUR LAND ...

"... this land is my land,
From California to the New York Island,
From the redwood forest, to the Gulf stream waters,
This land was made for you and me."

When Woody Guthrie wrote these words in 1940 as the opening to a song that now features in the National Recording Registry in the Library of Congress, it's said that he did so in exasperation at the popularity of the Irving Berlin song "God Bless America" in the run-up to the involvement of the USA in the Second World War. He originally termed it: God Blessed America.[1]

Reading four of the original six verses can make the song seem like a musical coast-to-coast tour of the United States and its natural beauty, but the other verses are different. One makes it plain that this is a protest song about restricted access to land and an encouragement to roam. The other makes it even plainer that it's a protest about economic conditions suffered by the dispossessed across the States. These verses are often omitted when this still-popular song is sung. There are strong echoes here of the themes in John Clare's poetry about the losses to ordinary people from the enclosure of common land.

This song is a good example of how popular music has been used to highlight socio-economic issues. An immediate comparison is with Ewan MacColl's "Manchester Rambler".[2] This 1932 song contrasts the joys of walking the high hills with the risks of encountering armed gamekeepers paid to protect their employers' land and shooting rights. It commemorates a mass trespass in the English Peak District which eventually led to more open access to land. Everpedia quotes MacColl as saying that his purpose in rambling was:

to create a world that would harmonize with that other one that you enjoyed so much … If the bourgeoisie had had any sense at all they would never have allowed the working class into that kind of countryside. Because it bred a spirit of revolt.[3]

This song was about land ownership and access, not about the environment or the social conditions of the working poor. Songs about that subject (which sometimes morph into anti-capital arguments) are a staple of the English folk music tradition. Many of these are songs passed down through an oral tradition and are of long standing. They became more frequent as industrialisation developed and people's socio-economic grievances grew. A prominent example from the 18th century is "The Hard Times of Old England";[4] another, from the 1820s, when post-Waterloo economic conditions were particularly harsh, is "The Four Loom Weaver", and "Poverty Knock" emerged around 1900 showing that poor working conditions persisted. Such songs are still being written today.

It took time for this music to address environmental issues, even though the settings – coal, cotton, iron – were giving rise to numerous environmental problems as the art and literature of the time show. Unless you count Blake's "Jerusalem" and its reference to "dark satanic mills",[5] it was only really in the late 20th century that such song themes emerged.

Tom Lehrer was an early exponent. His 1960s song "Pollution"[6] charts the American experience of uncontrolled emissions and spillages from heavy industry. Its message about air pollution still applies some 60 years on (and across the planet), though now increasingly because of diesel-powered vehicles, and power plants. Lehrer had difficulty getting his music played owing to the overtly political (if satirical) nature of his themes.

Another 1960s example is Joni Mitchell's "Big Yellow Taxi"[7] which noted that times were not always a'changing for the better because of the problems of urban development, and the industrial-scale use of pesticides in farming. The latter was a clear reference back to *Silent Spring*. [8] Public comments on Mitchell's own website have highlighted the way in which this oversimplified issues, citing the rise in malaria infections in developing countries that followed a widespread ban of the insecticide DDT because of the US-based campaign.

Songs aren't necessarily ideal for nuanced arguments. However, the lines in the chorus to "Big Yellow Taxi" which say that we don't understand and appreciate what we've got until it's gone, speak a universal truth that it seems we all have to learn for ourselves, sometimes more than once, and often only when it is too late.

The days of the high-profile environmental protest song seemed to have passed when, in the late 1970s, the Australian rock band Midnight Oil emerged as a hard-hitting proponent of environmental and social justice causes. The song "Progress" from their 1985 EP (extended play) single *Species Decreases*, includes lyrics that implore us to increase our awareness of the coming of "Manhattanization". Later, in England, Maggie Holland's songs "A Place Called England" and "A Proper Sort of Gardener"[9] encouraged a fightback against development and greed, and a re-building of community and shared values.

There are now thousands of such songs across cultures and they increasingly focus on global environmental matters such as climate change. Smokey Dymny's "Talkin' Global Warming Blues" (2002)[10] is a good example. It directly addresses the problems we all now face. Smokey knows who's responsible: it's corporations more powerful than individuals or communities.

Any review of this kind should include a part of Nicholas Mueller's 2009 witty "Environmental Evangelism Makes no Friends"[11] because it speaks of the difficulties faced by those wishing to make a difference to the world, as opposed to just their own lives. And also, because we think that humour (which is in short supply in earnest protest songs and in much real-world protesting as Yam et al. 2019 note) might just be a positive way of influencing people.

Finally, we should reference efforts to generate music using environmental data itself. An outstanding example is the work of data visualisation artist Brian Foo,[12] who creates music on all forms of data including the shrinking Mississippi delta and readings of air pollution. Data from smog have also been used by Greg Niemeyer of University of California, Berkeley and Chris Chafe of Stanford University who together have created jazz using data from some of the world's most polluted cities.[13] There is no sign of such data running out.

Notes

1 See this comment from americansongwriter.com/2012/06/behind-the-song-this-land-is-your-land
2 See: genius.com/Ewan-maccoll-manchester-rambler-lyrics
3 See: everipedia.org/wiki/lang_en/The_Manchester_Rambler
4 See: mainlynorfolk.info/copperfamily/songs/hardtimesofoldengland.html
5 Blake wrote the poem in 1804, but it was 1916 when Parry set it to music. Not everyone thinks that this should be taken literally as a reference to factories; some see such mills as Oxford and Cambridge Universities and their narrow curriculum. The lyric is here: songandpraise.org/and-did-those-feet-in-ancient-times-hymn.htm
6 There's a video on YouTube: tinyurl.com/yb37a4os
7 Here she is on YouTube: tinyurl.com/y4pqoym3
8 See Chapter 24.
9 See: maggieholland.co.uk
10 Lyrics and song here: unionsong.com/u462.html
11 Also on Union Songs: unionsong.com/u638.html
12 See: brianfoo.com
13 See: wired.com/2010/10/smog-music

Further reading

Yam, K.C., Barnes, C.M., Leavitt, K., Wei, W. & Uhlmann, E.L. (2019). Why so Serious? A laboratory and field investigation of the link between morality and humor. *Journal of Personality and Social Psychology*, 117 (4), 758–772.

PART II
Present imperfect

24

RACHEL CARSON'S SILENCE

"O what can ail thee, knight-at-arms
Alone and palely loitering?
The sedge has withered from the lake,
And no birds sing."[1]

The publication of Rachel Carson's *Silent Spring* in 1962[2] is popularly regarded as the dawn of the modern environmental movement – as the moment awareness of the serious impacts that we were making on the biosphere by how we lived began to be widely shared. *Silent Spring* was published to acclaim by conservationists but was roundly condemned by the US agro-chemical industry and by some in government, and Carson was the subject of considerable personal vilification.

The book accused the industry of dishonesty in the information it provided, and said that the government officials overseeing it were far too trusting. Although Carson's specific focus was the indiscriminate use of chemical pesticides in agriculture, and the effects they were having on wildlife, she also stressed the way that the public was patronised by those with authority:

> When the public protests, confronted with some obvious evidence of damaging results of pesticide applications, it is fed little tranquilizing pills of half-truth. We urgently need an end to these false assurances, to the sugar coating of unpalatable facts. It is the public that is being asked to assume the risks that the insect controllers calculate. The public must decide whether it wishes to continue on the present road, and it can do so only when in full possession of the facts. In the words of Jean Rostand, "The obligation to endure gives us the right to know".[3]

Carson[4] worked as a marine zoologist for the US Fish and Wildlife Service and it was a letter in *The Boston Herald* in 1958 that she said brought her "attention sharply back to a problem with which [she] had long been concerned",[5] and which led her to research the ways that powerful chemicals were being used before their impact on the biosphere was known. The book kick-started the US environmental movement and was a key factor in the setting up of the US Environmental Protection Agency (EPA) in 1970.

A significant part of the book relates to the use of DDT.[6] The book did not call for a ban on DDT. Rather, Carson asked for regulation, arguing that even if DDT and other insecticides had no side effects, their indiscriminate use was a problem because it would create insect resistance to pesticides, thus rendering them useless. However, in 1972, the EPA issued an order for the banning of DDT because of its adverse environmental effects on wildlife, and its potential human health risks. Following the US ban, international use of DDT rapidly ceased, which put a halt to one of the few effective ways of killing malarial mosquitoes which cause the deaths of hundreds of thousands of people every year.[7]

Today, DDT is still classified as a probable human carcinogen by international authorities. However, in 1986, the United Nations Environment Programme (UNEP) began to negotiate a treaty to ban or restrict persistent organic pollutants (POPs) such as DDT. This, the Stockholm Convention on POPs, came into force in 2004.[8] It provides a limited exemption for the use of DDT to control malarial mosquitoes. In 2006, the World Health Organization (WHO) supported the indoor use of DDT in African countries where malaria remains a major health problem, saying that benefits outweigh the health and environmental risks.

Paul A. Offit, writing in the *Daily Beast*, contends that in the period between the EPA ban and the Convention, tens of millions of people died needlessly from the disease, most being children under five.[9] He makes the point that while it was reasonable to have banned DDT for agricultural use, it was not reasonable to have eliminated it from public health use. He lays the blame for this on the impression that *Silent Spring* gives that DDT caused human illness and death. Where the responsibility for these deaths should lie remains a controversial issue.[10]

But *Silent Spring* was about much more than DDT. The US Natural Resources Defense Council[11] argues that "the most important legacy of *Silent Spring* was a new public awareness that nature was vulnerable to human intervention". It says that for the first time, the need to regulate industry in order to protect the environment became widely accepted, and environmentalism was born.

We'll give almost the last word to Rachel Carson herself. Appearing on a CBS documentary about *Silent Spring* shortly before her death in 1964, she said,[12]

> We still talk in terms of conquest. We still haven't become mature enough to think of ourselves as only a tiny part of a vast and incredible universe. Man's attitude toward nature is today critically important simply because we have now acquired a fateful power to alter and destroy nature. But man is a part of nature, and his war against nature is inevitably a war against himself. ... Now, I truly believe, that we in this generation, must come to terms with nature,

and I think we're challenged as mankind has never been challenged before to prove our maturity and our mastery, not of nature, but of ourselves.

Over 55 years on, we still haven't come to terms with our poor fit with nature and our need to master our own worst inclinations and the fateful power we have to alter and destroy. Today, this is being played out through climate change and the myriad alterations we have caused to biodiversity, mostly to its detriment.

The very last word goes to Pete Seeger who asked: When will we ever learn?[13]

Notes

1 This is a line from John Keats's "La Belle Dame sans Merci" which inspired the title of the book. See: tinyurl.com/y35yeow2
2 As we note elsewhere there are much earlier examples of social movements in 19th-century European industrial cities which gave rise to legislation to counter damaging air and water pollution. The educational focus of such movements was, of course, not directed towards young people in schools; rather, as with much sustainability-focused social activity today, it was sensibly aimed at politicians and informed public opinion.
3 *Silent Spring*, chapter 2, p. 13 (1962 edition).
4 See *The Life and Legacy of Rachel Carson* at: tinyurl.com/yyjn7o34
5 *Silent Spring*, Acknowledgements. The letter noted birds dying as a result of the use of aircraft to spray land with DDT to kill mosquitoes. As Carson noted, the result was "a small world made lifeless".
6 DDT is a powerful and wide-ranging insecticide first developed in 1939. In World War II it was used to clear Pacific islands of malaria-causing insects and used as a delousing powder in Europe. Its inventor was awarded a Nobel Prize. The Natural Resources Defense Council notes: "When DDT became available for civilian use in 1945, there were only a few people who expressed second thoughts about this new miracle compound. One was nature writer Edwin Way Teale, who warned, 'A spray as indiscriminate as DDT can upset the economy of nature as much as a revolution upsets social economy. Ninety percent of all insects are good, and if they are killed, things go out of kilter right away.' Another was Carson, who wrote to *Reader's Digest* to propose an article about a series of tests on DDT being conducted not far from where she lived in Maryland. The magazine rejected the idea." See: tinyurl.com/jcpngf5
7 The WHO estimates that 405,000 deaths due to malaria had occurred globally in 2018, of which 379,000 deaths (~94%) were in Africa. Almost 50% of all deaths in 2017 occurred in six countries in Africa and India. See: tinyurl.com/y5nx5dgj
8 The Stockholm Convention on Persistent Organic Pollutants was adopted on May 22, 2001 and entered into force on May 17, 2004. See: tinyurl.com/y6cb25dw
9 *The Daily Beast*: "How Rachel Carson Cost Millions of People Their Lives": tinyurl.com/y9tbhuj8
10 We think that some at least would accept that the EPA and other agencies should share some of the blame here, rather than it all belonging to a long-dead woman.
11 The Natural Resources Defense Council. See: tinyurl.com/jcpngf5
12 Rachel Carson In Memoriam: tinyurl.com/y4npyo6u
13 See YouTube at: tinyurl.com/y5nb4pdw

Further reading

Carson, R. (1962). *Silent Spring*. Boston: Houghton Mifflin.
Dillon, J. (2005). Silent Spring 40 Years on. *School Science Review*, 86, 316.

Lear, L. (2002). Rachel Carson and the Awakening of Environmental Consciousness. *Scholars Debate*. Web link: tinyurl.com/y6894oty

US Environmental Protection Agency. (n.d.). *DDT – A Brief History and Status*. Washington, DC: USEPA. Web link: tinyurl.com/hvtfnn3

25

THE ROAD TO TBILISI

"The Department of Education and Science claimed to have been encouraging environmental education all along – while taking care to absolve itself from any obligation to give any leadership in the future."[1]

As early as 1948, IUCN (the International Union for the Conservation of Nature)[2] was established in Paris,[3] but, as Disinger (1983/1997:18) noted, it was only in 1969 that "sufficient interest in environmental education as a 'new', discrete entity had emerged to occasion the development of definitional statements". At this time, the recognition[4] of the need for an educational response to our pressing environmental and social challenges prompted the promotion of environmental education as a significant concept, and this was formalised by IUCN at its conference in Carson City in 1970 as:

A process of recognising values and classifying concepts in order to develop skills and attitudes necessary to understand and appreciate the inter-relatedness among man, his culture and his biophysical surroundings.

IUCN added:

Environmental Education also entails practice in decision-making and self-formulating of a code of behaviour about issues concerning environmental quality.

Thus, environmental education was seen as going well beyond raising awareness of environmental or ecological issues; rather, it also was seen as focusing on the development of understandings of the relationships between humans, their culture and their environmental life-support systems. It was also felt that emphasising skills of citizenship and environmental responsibility in terms of social interaction, decision-making and positive behaviours was important. It is notable, even at this early stage, that the IUCN definition suggests that codes of behaviour should be self-formulated rather than socially determined or imposed.

However, in 1970, Stapp, in his three-pronged statement of objectives,[5] cautioned against the assumption that the possession of knowledge and skills would inevitably lead to changes in social behaviour. How right he was as research indicates that the link between increased knowledge and behaviour change is weak at best (Schultz 2011; and Marcinkowski & Reid 2019).

As we explore in another chapter, there were three other significant conferences in the 1970s that culminated in the Tbilisi Declaration.[6] These were:

- 1972 UN Conference on the Human Environment, in Stockholm
- 1975 UNESCO Environmental Education Conference, in Belgrade[7]
- 1977 UNESCO Intergovernmental Conference on Environmental Education, in Tbilisi

The Tbilisi Declaration strongly echoed the IUCN definition, stating that a basic aim of environmental education was:

> to succeed in making individuals and communities understand the complex nature of the natural and the built environments resulting from the interaction of their biological, physical, social, economic and cultural aspects, and acquire the knowledge, values, attitudes and practical skills to participate in a responsible and effective way in anticipating and solving environmental problems, and the management of the quality of the environment. (UNESCO-UNEP 1978)

Once again, the emphasis here is on understanding complex interactions and participation in resolving situations that arise from these relationships and the development of an active citizenry. As Stapp et al. (1979:92) put it, echoing the earlier work of Gary Harvey in his PhD,[8]

> the evolving goal of EE [environmental education] is to foster an environmentally literate global citizenry that will work together in building an acceptable quality of life for all people.

Harvey had actually advocated what he termed PERE (Person-Environment Relationship Education), which he defined as:

> the process of developing an environmentally literate, competent, and dedicated citizenry which actively strives to resolve values conflicts in the person-environment relationship, in a manner which is ecologically and humanistically sound, in order to reach the superordinate goal of a homeostasis between quality of life and quality of environment.

PERE was Harvey's preferred term for what everyone else was calling environmental education, and it's easy to see why it never caught on. It did, however, emphasise the idea that values conflicts would lie at the heart of many disputes and problems around our relationship with the natural world and that it would be through trying to resolve these that solutions might be found. Previously, the focus had been on the acquisition of appropriate values, and it still largely is; Harvey understood that such acquisition would usually involve the more difficult task of values change.[9]

This was not something that the authors of the Tbilisi environmental education goals understood. For them, acquisition was a key idea, and not just of values. Their goals were simply to:

1. foster clear awareness of, and concern about, economic, social, political and ecological interdependence in urban and rural areas
2. provide every person with opportunities to acquire the knowledge, values, attitudes, commitment and skills needed to protect and improve the environment
3. create new patterns of behaviour of individuals, groups and society as a whole towards the environment

These reflect Tbilisi's five categories of environmental education objectives,[10] which included helping social groups and individuals "acquire a set of values and feelings of concern for the environment and the motivation for actively participating in environmental improvement and protection".

In all this, the focus on the social as well as on the individual is striking in two senses. One, as England's school inspectorate (HMI 1979) noted, was that "There is an implicit progression from learning which is mainly directed towards personal development to learning which increasingly takes into account the needs of society". The other is the understanding that a resolution of environmental problems and dilemmas needs concerted social action as well as effort by individuals.

HMI added this in relation to curriculum and pedagogy:

> What is perhaps most important is to convey the realisation that environmental systems are complex and environmental problems not easily resolved. This cannot readily be done solely through the medium of individual subjects or without taking a synoptic view from time to time. The proper study of environmental issues requires cooperative teaching approaches and automatically entails cross-disciplinary reference.

This insight is still not widely understood.

Post-Tbilisi, environmental education was promoted most vigorously by NGOs, particularly in the economically developed global North, with WWF (formerly known as the World Wide Fund for Nature) being a prominent international agency for this. However, NGO policy proposals, as well as their specific educational resources, tended to reflect their own interests (in both senses), and this continues today. Their efforts tended to focus on developing good practice within a self-limiting conception of environmental education without contributing effectively to mainstream educational policy or practice in which the trend was towards increasing instrumentalism and economic rationalism.

It is unsurprising, therefore, that environmental education has struggled to shake off its association with the "green" environment and has often been confused with mere environmental studies. Indeed, Smyth (1995) suggested the adjective environmental had been a significant barrier to development as it distinguished environmental education from established disciplines, thereby placing it outside mainstream educational debates and practice. Much the same can be said of education for sustainable development (ESD), whose rise to prominence post-2002 contributed to a loss of focus on the essentials of environmental education: our dependence on the biosphere for our continuing existence.

Notes

1 See note 4.
2 It later changed its name to the World Conservation Union.
3 UK delegate Thomas Pritchard's speech at the conference is notable for a very early use of the term environmental education.
4 There are many examples of national and regional developments of an interest in environmental education during the 1960s. For one, punchy perspective on these, see Carson's 1978 *Environmental Education: Principles and Practice.* Commenting on a 1970 report in the UK, Sean Carson notes: "*and of course the Department of Education and Science claimed to have been encouraging environmental education all along – while taking care to absolve itself from any obligation to give any leadership in the future.*"
5 The objectives were: knowledge of environmental problems, awareness of possible solutions, and motivation towards solutions.
6 The Tbilisi Declaration can be downloaded here: ow.ly/6o1f3093yeJ. You have to negotiate a lot of UN-speak before you get to the core of the issues. There's a five-minute YouTube video of the conference here: ow.ly/oaat3093ytT. This is much better with the music and Russian language commentary turned off.
7 The Belgrade Charter was celebrated in the first edition of the Environmental Education Newsletter *Connect* (UNESCO-UNEP 1976) and was subtitled "a global framework for environmental education". It addressed a wide range of issues including guiding principles for environmental education programmes and objectives, and can be seen as a key development on the road to Tbilisi.
8 *Environmental Education: a delineation of substantive structure.* PhD thesis at Southern Illinois University at Carbondale. Dissertation Abstracts International 38 611-A, 1977. Whilst there is much richness in the Harvey definition of PERE, it is easy to see why Stapp et al. preferred a simpler version.
9 Harvey also noted that much of the environmental education literature is not about the person-environment relationship, but about "person-environment relationship foundations" (PERF), which are topics that provide learnings (psychomotor, cognitive, or affective) about the people-environment relationship, in a non-values-laden context. These are prerequisite, or complementary, to PERE.
10 The five Tbilisi environmental education objectives were to help social groups and individuals: acquire an awareness and sensitivity to the total environment and its allied problems; gain a variety of experience in, and acquire a basic understanding of, the

environment and its associated problems; acquire a set of values and feelings of concern for the environment and the motivation for actively participating in environmental improvement and protection; acquire the skills for identifying and solving environmental problems; and provide social groups and individuals with an opportunity to be actively involved at all levels in working toward resolution of environmental problems.

Further reading

Carson, S. McB. (Ed.). (1978). *Environmental Education: Principles and Practice*. London: Edward Arnold.

Disinger, J.F. (1983/1997). Environmental Education's Definitional Problem. *ERIC Clearinghouse for Science, Mathematics and Environmental Education Information Bulletin*, 2. Web link: tinyurl.com/yybls7pc

HMI. (1979). *Curriculum 11-16: Working papers by HM Inspectorate*. 2nd edition. London: Department of Education and Science. Web link: tinyurl.com/y6pm3k2r

IUCN. (1970). *International Working Meeting on EE in the School Curriculum. Final Report*. Gland, Switzerland: IUCN, UNEP and WWF.

Marcinkowski, T. & Reid, A. (2019). Editorial. *Environmental Education Research*, 25 (4), 459–471.

Schultz, P.W. (2011). Conservation means behaviour. *Conservation Biology*, 25, 1080–1083.

Smyth, J. (1995). Environment and Education: a view from a changing scene. *Environmental Education Research*, 1 (1), 1–20.

Stapp, W.B. (1970). Environmental Encounters. *Journal of Environmental Education*, 2 (1), 35–41.

Stapp, W.B. et al. (1979). Towards [a] National Strategy for Environmental Education. In A. B. Sacks & C.B. Davis (Eds.), *Current Issues in EE and Environmental Studies* (92–125). Columbus, OH: ERIC/SMEAC.

UNESCO-UNEP. (1976). *Connect Environmental Education Newsletter*, 1 (1). ERIC Number: ED179406. Web link: eric.ed.gov/?id=ED179406

UNESCO-UNEP. (1978). Inter-governmental Conference on Environmental Education, October 14–26, 1977, Tbilisi. Paris: UNESCO-UNEP.

26

GAIA

"We are sure that man needs Gaia, but could Gaia do without man? In man, Gaia has the equivalent of a central nervous system and an awareness of herself and the rest of the universe."[1]

In ancient Greek mythology, Gaia (or Gaea) was the god of the Earth who created herself out of chaos at the dawn of creation. She was viewed as the mother of everything including all the other Greek gods, with all mortal creatures being born of her flesh. The ancient Greeks saw the Earth as a flat disc surrounded by a river with the solid dome of heaven above. The disc rested on, and was inseparable from, Gaia's breast.

As we note elsewhere, this idea of Mother Earth or Earth Mother is very old and is widespread across the world's cultures. It embodies nature, motherhood, fertility, bounty and creation (and, it has to be said, sometimes also destruction). The Mother Earth idea still appeals to people now, and is especially beloved of many environmentalists who, whilst they might otherwise be quite irreligious, can find in the Earth a spiritual quality possibly missing from their lives. Their argument goes: if the Earth is literally the source of all goodness and nourishment, both spiritually and materially, should she not be respected, nurtured and generally looked after?

However, this is not the only way of thinking about such things, as James Lovelock illustrated when he first proposed his Gaia hypothesis in the late 1960s. This proposed that the Earth can be viewed as a single living functioning system. The hypothesis was then developed by Lynn Margulis in the 1970s and the two then worked together refining their ideas. They argued that all living organisms and their non-living environments are integrated within one system and that this is self-regulating, maintaining the appropriate conditions for life on Earth and for its survival. The system controls factors such as global temperature, atmospheric content and ocean salinity.[2]

In a 1975 article for *New Scientist,* Lovelock and Sidney Epton posed two questions: (i) do the Earth's living matter, air, oceans and land surface form part of a giant system which could be seen as a single organism?;[3] and (ii) could human activities reduce such a system's options so that it is no longer able to exert sufficient control to stay viable?

The first of these lies at the heart of the Gaia hypothesis; the second describes the existential threat we now pose to ourselves and to life itself. In their *New Scientist* article, Lovelock and Epton contrasted two propositions:

[1] life exists only because material conditions on Earth happen to be just right for its existence.

[2] life defines the material conditions needed for its survival and makes sure that they stay there.

Proposition 1, Lovelock and Epton say, is the conventional view that temperature, oxygen levels, humidity, ocean acidity and salinity, etc., fall within limits that mean that they are right for life to exist. Proposition 2 is the Gaia view which implies that "living matter is not passive in the face of threats to its existence. It has found means … of forcing conditions to stay within the permissible range".

Inherent in Proposition 2 is the idea that the components of the biosphere (air, oceans, ice, land) are in a kind of dynamic balance which maintains the sort of homeostatic condition that the human body manages with respect to temperature, blood pH, glucose levels, salinity, etc. For example, our temperature is controlled very close to 37°C even though it might be −20 or +45 outside. For Gaia, this means controlling within a narrow range atmospheric oxygen and carbon dioxide levels, ocean and soil pH, surface temperature, etc.

In many ways the idea of Gaia, with its proposition that what most of us regard as inanimate could in fact be thought of as somehow alive, remains as provocative as it was in the 1970s. Since that time, the hypothesis has given rise to many new areas of research about the Earth's physical, chemical, geological and biological processes, and these continue today. However, although it's useful to think of the Earth in systems terms, that doesn't mean it has to be the sort of living system that Lovelock first outlined, and many would now agree with Toby Tyrrell, a professor of Earth system science, when he says that the Gaia hypothesis is not an accurate picture of how our world works.[4]

That said, the idea and image of Gaia remain in the popular imagination with, for example, suggestions that we might view it in physiological terms: the Earth's oceans and rivers being its blood, the atmosphere its lungs, the land its bones, and living organisms its senses. Although this sort of imagery seems too literal a view of what is a sophisticated idea, Lovelock and Epton did end their *New Scientist* article with this:

Now for one more speculation. We are sure that man needs Gaia, but could Gaia do without man? In man, Gaia has the equivalent of a central nervous system and an awareness of herself and the rest of the universe. Through man, she has a rudimentary capacity, capable of development, to anticipate and guard against threats to her existence. For example, man can command just enough capacity to ward off a collision with a planetoid [asteroid] the size of Icarus. Can it then be that in the course of man's evolution within Gaia he has been acquiring the knowledge and skills necessary to ensure her survival?

Well, perhaps. But this leads us to wonder whether, if we are Gaia's central nervous system, we might be in the grip of a serious meningitis-like viral infection.[5] It was William Golding, the author of *Lord of the Flies* and a neighbour in Lovelock's village community, who suggested the name Gaia, and we wonder whether he had in mind that she had a reputation as something of a troublemaker amongst the gods.[6] We certainly think that it's by no means clear that a living Gaia would be eternally tolerant of a species – we humans – that constantly defied her both by its brute carelessness, and its hubris.

Notes

1 Quoted in *New Scientist* (February 6, 1975). See note 2.
2 You can listen to James Lovelock's brief explanation of Gaia here: tinyurl.com/y36ap57d
3 *New Scientist* (February 6, 1975). "The Quest for Gaia." Web link: tinyurl.com/y6h3ge3a
4 Tyrrell (2013).
5 Written before the advent of COVID-19, this refers specifically to the impact humanity is having on Gaia.
6 Golding (1954).

Further reading

Golding, W. (1954). *Lord of the Flies*. London: Faber & Faber.
Lovelock, J. (1979). *Gaia: A New Look at Life on Earth*. Oxford: Oxford University Press.
Lovelock, J. (1991). *Healing Gaia: Practical Medicine for the Planet*. Danvers, MA: Harmony Books.
Lovelock, J. (2006). *The Revenge of Gaia: Why the Earth Is Fighting Back – and How We Can Still Save Humanity*. Santa Barbara, CA: Allen Lane.
Lovelock, J. (2009). *The Vanishing Face of Gaia: A Final Warning: Enjoy It While You Can*. Santa Barbara, CA: Allen Lane.
Tyrrell, T. (2013). *On Gaia: A critical investigation of the relationship between life and Earth*. Princeton, NJ: Princeton University Press.

27

FOREST SCHOOL ORIGINS

"I don't have ADHD when I'm out in the woods."[1]

Forest schools as we know them today may have emerged relatively recently in Scandinavia, but the key ideas underpinning them have deep roots in ideas around nature and human learning.

The idea of the modern forest school began in Sweden with the work of Gösta Frohm who worked for the Swedish Outdoor Association – the Frilufts-främjandet[2] – developing its education and leadership programmes.[3] In 1957, noting that young children were becoming distanced from nature, he thought that providing sensory experiences outdoors, especially in the forest, would make up for the restrictions and limitations of modern living and reconnect them with the natural world. Frohm set up a *skogsmulle* school for five and six year olds, basing its practices around characters, stories and songs set in the outdoors.[4] The skogsmulle gave rise to a range of programmes for other age groups including the Swedish In Rain or Shine programme (*I Uur och Skur*), the *metsamoori* in Finland (also based around characters, stories and songs), and *frilufts barnehagein* in Denmark where it developed into an integral part of early years schooling. This realisation of an outdoor pedagogy for young children owed a lot to the influence of the German educationalist Friedrich Fröbel.[5]

The growth of forest schools in the UK stems from 1993 when staff from Bridgwater College in Somerset visited Danish forest kindergartens and were inspired by the way children developed through child-centred outdoor play. Geoffrey Guy makes a key point about the difference in culture between the UK and the less industrialised and populated Scandinavia where there is a widespread right to roam.[6] He notes that the UK had "evolved a culture biased heavily towards health and safety concerns and eliminating risk, as opposed to the Scandi-navian approach that appeared to treasure and embrace outdoor knowledge and 'friluftsliv' that is outdoor or fresh air life".[7] He also noted that UK agriculture and arboriculture had become industrialised and the majority of the increasingly urbanised working population had no need to spend time in nature other than for recreation.

That said, as Cree and McCree (2012/2013) point out, the UK has a rich history of seeing the importance of the natural world to the human experience of young and old alike. Amongst a range of influences they cite are: Wordsworth and Ruskin ("creative freedom, imagination, childhood innocence"); Baden-Powell (Scouting and Guiding); Margaret MacMillan's open-air movement and open-air schools in Edwardian London (with imaginative play inspired by Fröbel); Montessori's teachings on nursery education; the influence of Dewey and Piaget on Susan Isaacs's real-life learning journeys with outdoor play; the Woodcraft Folk (the skill of living in the open air close to nature); Gordonstoun (founded by Kurt Hahn); the Outward Bound Trust; the Field Studies movement; the Plowden Report which emphasised the value of play, the use of the outdoors, and learning by discovery with the child at the heart of the educational process; Playwork, seeing spontaneous play as essential; the development of adventure playgrounds; child studies and environmental education, encouraging children's voices and interaction in their local nature; Earth Education,[8] and sharing nature approaches.

Cree and McCree argue that the development of forest schools across the UK was helped by changes in society including the growth of environmental concern and the growing demand for natural play. As such, they continue to grow in popularity.[9]

Notes

1 This is a quote from 14-year-old David on the Forest Schools Association website. ADHD is attention deficit hyperactivity disorder. See: tinyurl.com/y4h5hllx
2 Literally: the fresh air foundation.
3 The association was established in 1892 to promote skiing. Over time, however, this extended to other outdoor activities.
4 Geoffrey Guy explores these issues in a blog: tinyurl.com/yxobmeyd
5 Fröbel was a German educationalist who had been a student of Pestalozzi. See Chapter 10. He created the idea of the kindergarten. See friedrichfroebel.com for a summary of his legacy.
6 In general, Scandinavian families are better prepared for harsh weather and enjoy more of an outdoor life.
7 We have a separate chapter on Friluftsliv.
8 Earth Education or *Acclimatization* was developed in the USA by the educationalist Steve van Matre. Emphasising ecological concepts, the use of the senses and a learner-centred pedagogy, it inspired urban wildlife groups in the late 1980s and remains popular with some environmental educationalists. See: earthed.org.uk
9 At the end of 2019, the UK Forest School Association (FSA, see: forestschoolassociation. org) estimated that there were some 5,000 qualified forest school leaders in the UK who worked in between 3,000 and 3,500 forest school settings. Membership of the FSA has grown from 200 (2014) to 2,000. For a view of what modern forest schools are doing see: tinyurl.com/y4h5hllx
10 *Horizons Magazine* is published by the Institute for Outdoor Learning: tinyurl.com/ y2vdj6b3

Further reading

Cree, J. & McCree, M. (2012). A Brief History of the Roots of Forest Schools in the UK Part 1. *Horizons Magazine*. *Institute of Outdoor Learning*. Web link: tinyurl.com/y5uzfyxg.[10]

Cree, J. & McCree, M. (2013). A Brief History of the Roots of Forest Schools in the UK Part 2. *Horizons Magazine*. *Institute of Outdoor Learning*. Web link: tinyurl.com/y2w732mh

Henderson, B. & Vikanger, N. (2007). *Nature First: Outdoor Life the Friluftsliv Way*. Canada: Natural Heritage Books.

Knight, S. (Ed.). (2013). *International Perspectives on Forest School: Natural spaces to play and learn*. London: Sage.

Louv, R. (2006). *Last child in the woods: Saving our children from nature-deficit disorder*. Chapel Hill, NC: Algonquin Books of Chapel Hill.

Ogilvie, K. (2012). *Roots and Wings – a history of outdoor education and outdoor learning in the UK*. London: Institute for Outdoor Learning.

Robertson, J. (2008a). *Swedish Forest Schools*. Creative Star Learning. Web link: tinyurl.com/y23jh49v

Robertson, J. (2008b). *I Ur och Skur Mulleborg and Skogsknattarna Forest Kindergartens*. Creative Star Learning. Web link: tinyurl.com/yx9qfy7r

28

THE EARLY UN CONFERENCES

"Sustainability is not a concept referring to some static paradise, but rather a capacity of human beings to continuously adapt to their non-human environments by means of social organisation."[1]

Beginning in 1972, the world saw a series of international gatherings and UN conferences and meetings that focused on environment, sustainability and education. Figure 1 shows these alongside concurrent educational initiatives in England.

The United Nations Conference on the Human Environment (Stockholm, 1972), was the second of these international meetings that eventually led to the Earth Summits in 1992, 2002 and 2012. Its outcomes reflected rather an instrumental view recommending environmental education as a measure "for the understanding, protection and improvement of the environment and its quality" (Sato 2006:1), although it did also set in train preparations for the 1975 International Environmental Education workshop in Belgrade, and the Intergovernmental Conference on Environmental Education in Tbilisi in 1977.

The Belgrade Charter, which emerged from the International Environmental Education workshop, was celebrated in the first edition of the Environmental Education Newsletter *Connect* (UNESCO-UNEP 1976) and was subtitled "a global framework for environmental education". It addressed a wide range of issues including guiding principles for environmental education programmes and objectives, and can be seen as a staging post on the way to Tbilisi and its Declaration. As we note elsewhere, this stated that a basic aim of environmental education was:

> to succeed in making individuals and communities understand the complex nature of the natural and the built environments resulting from the interaction of their biological, physical, social, economic and cultural aspects, and acquire the knowledge, values, attitudes and practical skills to participate in a

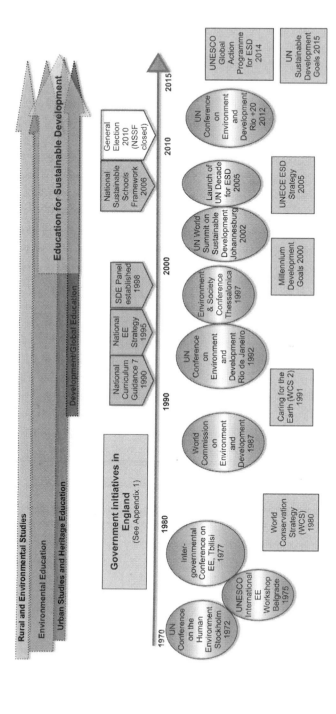

FIGURE 1 International conferences related to learning and environment (plus some international strategies)

responsible and effective way in anticipating and solving environmental problems, and the management of the quality of the environment. (UNESCO-UNEP 1978)

It is clear from this that the "curriculum" of environmental education clearly aims to go well beyond knowledge and an important goal is the development of an active citizenry.

During the 1980s, environmental education was promoted most vigorously by NGOs, particularly in the economically developed global North, with WWF being a prominent international agency for this. However, NGO policy proposals, as well as their specific educational resources, tended to reflect their own interests (this continues today) and their efforts have tended to focus on developing good practice within a self-limiting conception of environmental education without contributing significantly to mainstream educational policy or practice where the trend has been towards increasing instrumentalism and economic rationalism. It is unsurprising, therefore, that environmental education has struggled to shake off its association with the "green" environment and has often been confused with environmental studies.

By the 1990s environmental education was ripe for re-casting as an enterprise of broader scope and it was at this time that sustainable development was gaining traction as an idea. *Our Common Future* (WCED 1987, *The Brundtland Report*) describes sustainable development in this way:

> development that meets the needs of the present without compromising the ability of future generations to meet their own needs. It contains within it two key concepts:
> the concept of "needs", in particular the essential needs of the world's poor, to which overriding priority should be given; and the idea of limitations imposed by the state of technology and social organization on the environment's ability to meet present and future needs. (WCED 1987: chapter 2, paragraph 1)[2]

As Sauvé notes, in Scott and Gough (2004:145), the definition itself was a compromise (though presented as a consensus), arrived at after references to "environment" and concepts such as "eco-development" were "discarded because [they were] an irritant for many participants: the focus had to be on (economic) development". The resulting definition aims to square the circle between economic growth and environmental protection, although a technicist orientation is evident from the notion that limitations are imposed by the "state of technology", as well as by environmental limits. As such, it is unsurprising that Bonnett (2007:170), speaking for many and echoing the earlier concerns of the philosopher Martin Heidegger, viewed sustainable development with suspicion because of its:

> highly anthropocentric and economic motives that lead to nature being seen essentially as a resource.

However, the Brundtland Commission stressed that sustainable development is a process of change with the future in mind:

> A process where the exploitation of resources, the orientation of technological development and institutional change, are made consistent with future as well as present needs.

Hamm and Muttagi (1998:2), in their book on sustainable development and the future of cities, put it like this:

> Sustainability is not a concept referring to some static paradise, but rather a capacity of human beings to continuously adapt to their non-human environments by means of social organisation.

These authors see sustainable development as a process through which we shall need to learn to live more in tune with the environment. However, it is not enough to say that sustainable development and such learning need to go hand in hand. Rather, it is crucial to recognise that sustainable development will not be taking place where learning is not happening. To put this another way: sustainable development is a learning process through which we can (if we choose) learn to build our capacity to live more sustainably, and to learn from the future as it emerges (Foster 2008; and Scharmer 2009).

There is little emphasis here on teaching for two reasons: the first is that much of the learning we shall need to do will be beyond the school, college, and university system; it will be learning in, between and by institutions, organisations and communities – where most of our learning goes on anyway. The second is that as we don't yet know what exactly we shall need to learn in relation to sustainable development, it's hard to know in detail what needs to be taught – except, perhaps, how to learn.

For us, Hamm and Muttagi (op. cit.:2) make a crucial distinction:

> Sustainable development is essentially not about the environment, but rather about the capacity of human society to enact permanent reform in order to safeguard the delicate balance between humans and their natural life-support system.

This is concerned with building our capacity to live, and our capacity to learn. However, if from a technical viewpoint we view nature as a possible guide and framework from which to build sustainable consumption and production patterns,[3] then nature study, the very bedrock of early environmental education, becomes an essential component of this ongoing, society-wide learning process.[4]

Notes

1   Quoted in Hamm and Muttagi (1998).

2 It is all too common to find only the first 20 words quoted, omitting the hugely significant qualifying text that follows.
3 As, for example, proposed by the *Ellen MacArthur Foundation*: ellenmacarthurfoundation. org
4 The fact Forest Schools (forestschools.com) are growing quickly in the UK may be a good thing, and such a connection with nature may become a national entitlement, rather than the loosely defined "outdoor experience". However, this will only likely be so if the nature that is studied focuses on social as well as ecological issues.

Further reading

Bonnett, M. (2007). Environmental education and the issue of nature. *Journal of Curriculum Studies*, 39 (6), 707–721.

Foster, J. (2008). *The Sustainability Mirage*. London: Earthscan.

Hamm, B. & Muttagi, P.K. (1998). *Sustainable Development and the Future of Cities*. London: Intermediate Technology Publications.

Sato, M. (2006). *Evolving Environmental Education and its relation to EPD and ESD: Overview of the Conceptual Development based on a series of International Discussions on Environmental Education*. Paper presented at the UNESCO Expert Meeting on ESD, in May 2006 in Kanchanaburi, Thailand.

Scharmer, O. (2009). *Theory U: Learning from the Future as it Emerges*. San Francisco, CA: Berrett-Koehler.

Scott, W. & Gough, S.R. (2004). *Key Issues in Sustainable Development and Learning*. London: Routledge.

UNESCO-UNEP. (1976). *Connect*, 1 (1), 1.

UNESCO-UNEP. (1978). Inter-governmental Conference on Environmental Education, October 14–26, 1977, Tbilisi. Paris: UNESCO-UNEP.

World Commission on Environment and Development (WCED). (1987). *Our Common Future*. Oxford: Oxford University Press.

29

PREPOSITIONS AND THE ENVIRONMENT

"It is the emphasis on attitude formation that leads to some disagreements concerning the propriety of attempting to 'educate for the environment'."[1]

In their review of environmental education in secondary schools in England, Glackin and King (2018a:8), write:

> The point that, ideologically, teachers see environmental education as a cross-curricular subject, and operating at various levels, chimes with the argument of Lucas (1972) who defined environmental education as being: education in, about and for the environment.[2]

Glackin and King saw these as "environmental education's three underpinning values" in relation to knowledge, skills and social activism. The use of these prepositions as a means of differentiating aspects of environmental education remains strong, as this introduction to a recent (NAEE 2017) curriculum review shows:

> Environmental education helps to foster caring, responsible attitudes and inspires young people to take action in order to live more sustainably. ... There are three interrelated components ...
>
> Education IN the environment – using children's immediate surroundings and the wider world as a learning resource. This can be thought of as the "hands-on" element.
>
> Education ABOUT the environment – developing knowledge and understanding about the environment should begin with an awareness of the local environment and then extend to an understanding of global environmental issues.

Education FOR the environment – the development of positive attitudes and behaviours towards the environment. This can only be effective if the other two elements are in place.

Such terms have been a persistent feature of environmental education rhetoric since the late 1960s and, as the quotation at the head of this chapter notes, they have also been a source of disputation.[3] As we explore elsewhere, this was primarily because some argued that education for the environment should be seen as paramount because it is only through social change that the natural world can be saved from humanity.[4]

It was perhaps inevitable that such prepositions would come to be used in differentiating between aspects of environmental education. In 1969, George Martin noted that "It is the value of the contribution to our culture which environmental studies can make, using the environment for education and education for the environment, which must be judged".[5]

In 1970, a report from the Council for Environmental Education (CEE) introduced an important distinction:

some stress the educational value of using man's [sic] biological and physical environment as a basis for studies at first-hand, viewing this environment as a *medium for education*; while others are more concerned with the need to promote a sense of personal responsibility for the state of the environment, which is thus seen as a *goal of education*.[6]

Lucas, in his PhD thesis (Lucas 1972:128), took this a step further:

Environmental education may refer to one of, or any combination of, education about, for (the preservation of), or in the environment. The first two primary classes are distinguished by their goals: education about the environment aims at producing a knowledgeable individual; education for the environment is intended to enhance or maintain the environment of the entity, usually human, being considered. Education in the environment, by contrast, is a description of a pedagogic technique. In most cases where environmental education refers to "education in the environment", "environment" is intended to mean "outside the classroom".[7]

Lucas also said that environmental education could be classified into the "classes formed by the combinations *about* and *for*, *about* and *in*, and *for* and *in*". This is borne out in real life as countless studies of practice illustrate. There has also been an interpretation that sees *about/for/in* in an embodied way:

- the head: education *about*
- the heart: education *for*
- the hands: education *in*[8]

A more recent iteration of education in the environment is learning outside the classroom which the Council for Learning Outside the Classroom (CLOtC)[9] sees as a tool for teaching and learning which "has been proven to raise attainment and achievement, improve behaviour and improve the engagement of all groups of pupils, including those who are hard to engage inside the classroom environment".

All this illustrates a range of interpretations and possibilities; some goal-focused, others not: using the environment …

- as a learning resource
- as a tool for learning
- as a medium for learning
- to provide an opportunity to use particular pedagogical techniques
- to develop practical and other skills[10]

Fifty years on from Martin and Lucas, being in the (natural) environment is now said by many groups to be a goal in itself simply because it is seen to be good for young and not so young people's well-being, as research studies consistently show.[11]

For a range of reasons, many children across the Western world are now spending much less time outdoors, resulting, it is said, in a range of problems from obesity to poor mental health. This has given rise to a determined attempt to reverse this trend. The growth of Forest Schools (which rarely have anything to do with forest ecology but do emphasise being outside), are an indication of this tendency. In the USA, a condition termed nature deficit disorder was diagnosed by Louv in 2005.[12] White et al. (2019) argue that there is a growing body of epidemiological evidence which indicates that greater exposure to, or contact with, natural environments (such as parks, woodlands and beaches) is associated with better health and well-being, at least among populations in high-income, largely urbanised, societies. See for example, Martin Seligman's model of well-being, PERMA, which sets out five important building blocks of well-being and happiness.[13] Given this emphasis on getting young people to spend more time out of doors largely for health and well-being reasons, where merely being there is a large part of the benefit, it is easy to see why *in the environment* has become associated with place and not with pedagogy or particular goals.

This seems fine if your purpose relates to health and well-being. However, if your goal is (environmentally) educational, then goals matter a great deal as what you learn in relation to understanding and skills, and what you assimilate in relation to positive attitudes, dispositions and values are crucial. In such circumstances learning *in* the environment can be justified for at least five reasons:

- Learning is not possible unless you are there – for example, the development of practical ecology skills where first-hand experience is necessary
- Learning is more likely to be more effective there than elsewhere – for example, the study of geomorphology in situ

- Learning is just as effective there as in the classroom but there are other benefits – for example, fresh air, exercise and a degree of informality
- Learning out of the classroom is justified because it affords an immediacy and authenticity that is not possible elsewhere – for example, an outdoor biological recording class
- Learning of all kinds, some of which will be unpredictable, will only be possible when you are in nature[14]

All that said, it's clear that for some, being in the natural environment (nature) will always be its own justification.

Notes

1 Arthur Lucas's prescient and understated comment on the controversies inherent in educating for the environment is included in his PhD thesis (1972:128).
2 They went on: "several respondents suggested that education about the environment is primarily addressed in the science curriculum, whilst education for the environment is primarily addressed in geography, citizenship, PSHE [Personal, Social, Health Education] and RE [Religious Education]. Education in the environment could be enacted across all subjects."
3 There has also been confusion around the relationships between in, about and for.
4 See the chapter on the behaviour of models for a detailed comment on this.
5 Martin was first Chair of the Society for Environmental Education and was speaking in Leicester at the first conference of the Society. This quote comes from Martin and Wheeler (1975:9).
6 This quote also comes from Martin and Wheeler (1975:10).
7 Lucas's use of "knowledge" included both knowledge *of what* and knowledge *of how* and took in cognitive understanding and the development of skills necessary to obtain this understanding.
8 Susan A. Fenoughty; personal communication. See our chapter on Patrick Geddes for another perspective on this.
9 The CLOtC definition is here: lotc.org.uk/what-is-lotc
10 This list might be compared to Scott and Gough's (2003) categories of interest in our chapter on environmental learning. The prime purpose of the article was to identify the range of learning foci arising from human encounters with the environment that they had seen represented at NAAEE (North American Association for Environmental Education) conferences.
11 A 2019 study (White et al.) found that people who spend at least 120 minutes in nature a week are significantly more likely to report good health and higher psychological well-being than those who don't. See: tinyurl.com/y3jc4vme
12 The disorder is not recognised clinically. See the Children & Nature Network (C&NN) for more detail: childrenandnature.org. C&NN's strategic agenda (2017–2010) is here: tinyurl.com/y6hupn6u. There is no evidence of an emphasis on pedagogy.
13 According to Seligman, PERMA makes up five important building blocks of well-being and happiness: **P**ositive emotions – feeling good; **E**ngagement – being completely absorbed in activities; **R**elationships – being authentically connected to others; **M**eaning – purposeful existence; and **A**chievement – a sense of accomplishment and success. See: tinyurl.com/yxhzt6jw
14 This is an example of Wordsworth's injunction to "let nature be your teacher". See also our chapter on Friluftsliv.

Further reading

CEE. (1970). *Report No. 9*. Reading: Council for Environmental Education.

Glackin, M. & King, H. (2018a). *Understanding Environmental Education in Secondary Schools in England: the practitioners' perspectives*. King's College London/British Academy. Web link: tinyurl.com/y7cunql9as

Glackin, M. & King, H. (2018b). *Understanding Environmental Education in Secondary Schools in England: perspectives from policy*. King's College London/British Academy. Web link: tinyurl.com/ybgxf7ye

Louv, R. (2005). *Last Child in the Woods: Saving Our Children from Nature-Deficit Disorder*. Chapel Hill, NC: Algonquin Books.

Lucas, A.M. (1972). *Environment and environmental education: conceptual issues and curriculum implications*. PhD dissertation, The Ohio State University. *Dissertation Abstracts International*, 33 (6064-A). UMI Order No. 73-11, 531. Web link: eric.ed.gov/?id=ED068371

Martin, G.C. & Wheeler, K. (Eds.). (1975). *Insights into Environmental Education*. Edinburgh: Oliver & Boyd.

National Association for Environmental Education (NAEE). (2017). *Opportunities for Environmental Education across the National Curriculum for England Early Years Foundation Stage & Primary*. Web link: tinyurl.com/ybd7zuk8

Scott, W. & Gough, S.R. (2003). Using the environment as a stimulus to learning: exploring categories of interest. *Environmental Communicator*, 33 (1), 8.

White, M.P., Alcock, I., Grellier, J., Wheeler, B.W., Hartig, T., Warber, S.L., Bone, A., Depledge, M.H. & Fleming, L.E. (2019). Spending at least 120 minutes a week in nature is associated with good health and wellbeing. *Scientific Reports*, 9 (7730). Web link: tinyurl.com/uaree3c

30

HOW DEEP IS YOUR ECOLOGY?

"We don't say that every living being has the same value as a human, but that it has an intrinsic value which is not quantifiable. It is not equal or unequal. It has a right to live and blossom. I may kill a mosquito if it is on the face of my baby but I will never say I have a higher right to life than a mosquito."[1]

The injunction to live as if nature mattered was set out in detail by Devall and Sessions (1985) and developed from the thinking of Arne Naess, a Norwegian philosopher and explorer. Naess had coined the phrase *deep ecology* in 1973 to mark what he saw as a distinct turn in grassroots environmentalism towards a new form of ecological consciousness.[2] The contribution of deep ecology was to recognise the inherent value of all living beings, and then to use this insight to try to shape environmental policies.

Here "deep" describes the extent of the questioning needed of purposes and values when analysing contexts, problems and solutions. This involves examining fundamental issues and root causes, and then redesigning whole systems based on values and methods that preserve the ecological and cultural diversity of natural systems. Supporters of deep ecology are unified by an understanding of what needs to be done to protect ecological communities and ecocentric values.

These are the original Deep Ecology Platform principles:[3]

1. The well-being and flourishing of human and nonhuman life on Earth have value in themselves (synonyms: inherent worth, intrinsic value, inherent value). These values are independent of the usefulness of the nonhuman world for human purposes.
2. Richness and diversity of life forms contribute to the realization of these values and are also values in themselves.

3.   Humans have no right to reduce this richness and diversity except to satisfy vital needs.
4.   Present human interference with the nonhuman world is excessive, and the situation is rapidly worsening.
5.   The flourishing of human life and cultures is compatible with a substantial decrease of the human population.
6.   The flourishing of nonhuman life requires such a decrease.
7.   Policies must therefore be changed. The changes in policies affect basic economic, technological, and ideological structures. The resulting state of affairs will be deeply different from the present.
8.   The ideological change is mainly that of appreciating life quality (dwelling in situations of inherent worth) rather than adhering to an increasingly higher standard of living. There will be a profound awareness of the difference between big and great.
9.   Those who subscribe to the foregoing points have an obligation directly or indirectly to participate in the attempt to implement the necessary changes.

By contrast, Drengson says, shallow ecology doesn't go as far as this, usually promoting technological fixes (e.g. recycling, increased efficiency, organic agriculture) based on the same consumption-oriented values and approaches of the industrial economy. It remains, at its core, exploitative of natural systems. This is essentially business as usual for humanity. Drengson argues that the deep ecology principles entail a commitment to respecting the intrinsic values of richness and diversity and a rejection of our industrial culture, whose development models construe the Earth only as raw materials to be used to satisfy production and consumption.

Deep ecology has influenced many environmental action groups across the world, particularly those interested in harmony between humans and the rest of the biosphere. In one sense, the warning it sets out about the future is more apt now, 35 years on, even if there is no mention of global warming and climate change, the backcloth against which all other dramas are now being enacted, or of specifics such as the loss of biodiversity, habitat and species. But the principles at the heart of deep ecology have been widely criticised, as the following brief points illustrate:[4]

1.   Principle 3 of deep ecology says that humans have no right to reduce the Earth's richness and diversity except to satisfy vital needs. But what's to count as vital? Are these what we need to subsist as an animal, or to thrive, culturally, as a human? And who's to say? Using the word vital as if it had clarity, is just to side-step the unresolved needs/wants debate.
2.   Further, taken to its logical limit, not disturbing richness and diversity implies that there is some sort of equivalence between humans and, say, a bacterium. Even the bacterium might think (if it could) that this is absurd. It is more plausible to claim that deep ecology's principles are just human values imposed through a romantic view of nature.

3.   Luke (2003) notes that deep ecology is grounded in a belief that industrial society cannot conquer scarcity and so a programme is needed of self-sacrifice, and voluntary simplicity in which we live close to nature in a "spare economy of basic survival." Not many share this view, even if they are sceptical of the role that technology can play in helping us to become more sustainable.[5]

4.   Ross (1994), was a vocal critic of deep ecology because of what he saw as its presumption that nature knows best. He says that nature offers no useful models for human well-being and is against the idea that nature should become the referee of our fate because, as Luke notes, of the risk to human rights, individual freedoms, and communal liberties.

5.   Bookchin, the social ecologist, claimed the philosophy came mainly from pale, male academics and their students, and that its concerns were akin to New Age occultism with undertones of paganism, that we usually associate with quasi-fascist Aryan social movements.

6.   Deep ecology implies that we might learn from indigenous hunter-gatherers' values and practices that can help us to dwell wisely in the world. However, the individuals within such groups are not necessarily more ecocentric than the average human.

7.   And finally, what about the global population whose reduction was core to the original deep ecology principles? Not even Naess could come up with a plausible way of doing this that was morally supportable.

Notes

1   Arne Naess quoted in a *Guardian* obituary: tinyurl.com/yyw7ctsc
2   Environmentalism had evolved through the 1960s as a loose political movement stimulated by Rachel Carson's *Silent Spring* and of course by previous writers and activists such as Thoreau, Muir and Leopold. At this time, many were becoming concerned about the detrimental environmental effects of industrial technology.
3   See: deepecology.org/platform.htm
4   www.thegreenfuse.org sets out an extensive critique of deep ecology.
5   Whilst it's tempting to see this view as extreme, this would run the risk of seeing it as extremist; perhaps, it's better to see it as an outlier on a spectrum of ideas which propose that we live within the grain of nature.

Further reading

Bookchin, M. (1987). Social Ecology versus Deep Ecology: A Challenge for the Ecology Movement. *Green Perspectives: Newsletter of the Green Program Project*, 4–5. Web link: tinyurl.com/y4vb393s
Devall, B. (1988). *Simple in Means, Rich in Ends: Practicing Deep Ecology*. Salt Lake City, UT: Peregrine Smith Books.
Devall, B. & Sessions, G. (1985). *Deep Ecology: living as if nature mattered*. Salt Lake City, UT: Peregrine Smith Books.
Drengson, A. (n.d.). *Some Thought on the Deep Ecology Movement*. San Francisco, CA: The Foundation for Deep Ecology. Web link: deepecology.org/deepecology.htm

Luke, T.W. (2003). Humans and Nature: Tensions and Interdependence. In W. Scott & S. Gough (Eds.), *Key Issues in Sustainable Development and Learning: a critical review*. London: Routledge.

Ross, A. (1994). *The Chicago gangster theory of life; Nature's debt to society*. New York, NY: Verso.

31

ENVIRONMENTALLY EDUCATED TEACHERS

"What of the role of the … environmentally educated teacher in the vital process of education …? Is it not, arguably, the priority of educational and, certainly, environmental priorities …?"[1]

Ministers at the 1977 Tbilisi Conference concluded that environmental education should be an obligatory part of pre- and in-service teacher education and pertinent to the area where the teacher was going to practise. Ten years later, Volume 25 of UNESCO-UNEP's International Environmental Education Programme (IEEP) (Wilke et al. 1987)[2] set out competencies[3] that an environmentally educated teacher ought to have. Another 30 years on, we are still waiting for their widespread adoption.

Two kinds of competency were proposed: (i) foundational ones in professional education, and (ii) competencies in environmental education (EE) content. These were helpfully summarised in 1990 in the first edition of UNESCO's newsletter, *Connect*.

The authors of Volume 25 prefaced their setting out of the competencies with this statement:

It may be expected that teachers at all levels and in various disciplines may require more or less competency in some of the following areas. A secondary social studies teacher, for example, may require more expertise in the use of case studies as investigative models than is required by a primary level teacher. However, the need for some degree of competency in each of the areas, will remain for all effective EE teachers. The following statements should be interpreted as defining areas of competency which may be used to guide the planning stages of an EE teacher training programme. The competencies must be further refined into more specific statements if they are to be functional in selecting topics, teaching strategies, or evaluation schemes for the training programme.[4]

Thus, the competences were seen as both universal in applicability, but only as starting points for contextually appropriate professional development. These are the competency statements:

Foundational competencies in professional education
The effective environmentally educated teacher should be able to:

- apply a knowledge of educational philosophy to the selection or development of curricular programmes and strategies to achieve both general education and EE goals.

  (General education materials and methods may sometimes need merely to be "environmentalized" to achieve both objectives)

- utilize current theories of moral reasoning in selecting, developing and implementing EE curricula which will effectively achieve EE goals.

  (Teachers should be competent to use appropriate strategies to allow learners to recognize the role of values in environmental decision making, clarify value positions and understand the valuing process)

- utilize current theories of knowledge/attitude/behavior relationships in selecting, developing and implementing a balanced curriculum which maximizes the probability of desired environmentally aware behavior changes in learners.

  (A balanced curriculum takes into account such aspects as ecological factors vs. trade-off costs, etc.)

- utilize current theories of learning in selecting, developing and implementing curricular strategies to effectively achieve EE goals.

  (The methodology of EE as well as the nature of many EE goals is problem solving. A pragmatic approach on the part of teachers to theories of learning development, such as Piaget's, can do much to increase EE effectiveness in such methodologies and goals as environmental problem solving)

- apply the theory of transfer of learning in selecting, developing and implementing curricular materials and strategies to insure that learned knowledge, attitudes and cognitive skills will be transferred to the learner's choices and decision making concerning lifestyle and behavior.

  (The ultimate goal of EE is to produce environmentally literate citizens who are willing and capable of taking positive environmental actions in their lifetime)

- effectively implement the following methodologies to achieve EE goals:

  - interdisciplinarity, outdoor education, values clarification, games and simulation, case-study approaches, community resource use, autonomous student and/or group investigation, evaluation and action in environmental problem solving, and appropriate teacher behaviors when handling controversial environmental issues;
  - develop and use effective means of planning for instruction
  - effectively infuse appropriate EE curricula and methods into all disciplines to which the teacher is assigned
  - effectively evaluate the results of EE curricula and methods in both cognitive and affective domains.

Competencies in environmental education content
Level I: Ecological foundations
The effective environmentally educated teacher should be able to:
- apply a knowledge of ecological foundations to the analysis of environmental issues and identify key ecological principles involved
- apply a knowledge of ecological foundations to predict the ecological consequences of alternative solutions to environmental problems
- be sufficiently literate in ecology to identify, select and interpret appropriate sources of scientific information in a continuing effort to investigate, evaluate and find solutions for environmental problems
- communicate and apply in an educational context the major concepts in ecology.

Level II: Conceptual awareness
The effective environmentally educated teacher should be able to select, develop and implement curricular materials which will make learners aware of:
- how people's cultural or vocational activities (economic, religious, industrial, etc.) affect the environment from an ecological perspective
- how individual behaviors impact on the environment from the same perspective
- a wide variety of local, regional, national and international environmental issues and the ecological and cultural implications of these issues
- the viable alternative solutions available for remediating discrete environmental issues and the ecological and cultural implications of these alternative solutions
- the need for environmental issue investigation and evaluation as a prerequisite to sound decision making
- the roles played by differing human values clarification as an integral part of environmental decision making
- the need for responsible citizenship action (persuasion, consumerism, legal action, political action, eco-management, etc.) in the remediation of environmental concerns.

Level III: Investigation and evaluation

The effective environmentally educated teacher should be competent to investigate environmental issues and evaluate alternative solutions and to develop, select and implement curricular materials and strategies which will develop similar competencies in learners, including:

- the knowledge and skills needed to identify and investigate issues (using both primary and secondary sources of information and to synthesize the data gathered)
- the ability to analyze environmental issues and the associated value perspectives with respect to their ecological and cultural implications
- the ability to identify alternative solutions for discrete issues and the value perspectives associated with these solutions
- the ability to autonomously evaluate alternative solutions and associated value perspectives for discrete environmental issues with respect to their cultural and ecological implications
- the ability to identify and clarify their own value positions related to discrete environmental issues and their associated solutions
- the ability to evaluate, clarify and change their own value positions in the light of new information.

Level IV: Environmental action skills

The effective environmentally educated teacher should be competent to take positive environmental action for the purpose of achieving and maintaining a dynamic equilibrium between the quality of life and the quality of the environment (if indeed one can be separated from the other) and develop similar competencies in learners to take individual or group action when appropriate, such as persuasion, consumerism, political action, legal action, eco-management or combinations of these categories of action.

The foundation competences in professional education are a mixture of environmental education-specific competences, and more mainstream ones which have had an environmental element grafted on to them. Despite their origins in USA-based thinking about environmental education, anyone training to be a teacher in the 1970s and 1980s in the English-speaking world would likely recognise the thinking behind what is written. Further, the focus on curriculum development based around learning theories and on classroom planning based on moral development theories would likely have been common to a wider audience.

Despite the caveats expressed in the original authors' preface (above), it would be a remarkable pre-service programme that could do all this, given how short many of these now are, given everything else that has to be included, and given the manifest lack of knowledge, understanding and skills amongst tutors.

Although the foundational competency statements are wide-ranging in scope, dealing with them might not be too problematic, given the mainstream nature of their core contents. When it comes to competencies in EE content, however, the problems multiply. Level 1 looks rather like a degree course in ecology, and Levels 2 to 4 resemble an EE degree programme. As such, it is perhaps no small wonder that not much came of this ambitious proposal at the time, particularly given the top-down nature of it.

Significantly, however, with the worldwide calls for education programmes (and teacher training to support them) that take the climate and ecological crises seriously, authorities might well think that the time for such a programme has come.[5]

Notes

1 Quoted from UNESCO-UNEP (1990). This is usually abbreviated to the proposition that preparing the environmentally educated teachers should be the priority of priorities.
2 The background to the programme can be seen here: tinyurl.com/y3sqnd44. It was produced as a series of green A4 booklets which enjoyed wide circulation and can probably be found in many university libraries. The contents of Vol. 25 is here: tinyurl.com/yykz48rn
3 Wilke *et al.* use the term competency; we differentiate between *competencies* and *competences* in Chapter 39.
4 The authors said that the text in parentheses that follows the competency statements were "Narratives which are intended to exemplify and facilitate the refinement process follow many of the competency area statements".
5 See teachthefuture.uk as an example of the many calls for action around the curriculum.

Further reading

UNESCO-UNEP. (1990). Environmentally educated teachers the priority of priorities? *Connect*, XV (1), 1–3.
Wilke, R.J., Peyton, R.B. & Hungerford, H.R. (1987). *Strategies for the training of teachers in environmental education*. International Environmental Education Programme; environmental education series No. 25. Paris: UNESCO-UNEP.

32

ARE SIGNIFICANT LIFE EXPERIENCES ALWAYS SIGNIFICANT?

"If we can identify the most significant life experiences to have, we can ensure that everyone has them."[1]

In 1980, Thomas Tanner published a ground-breaking paper in the *Journal of Environmental Education* which started a new line of research inquiry. This began with a quote from Walt Whitman's "Leaves of Grass":[2]

There was a child went forth every day,
And the first object he looked upon that object he became ...[3]

Tanner (1980:20) understood that environmental sensitivity was one of several variables that contribute to the creation of citizens who will work to maintain "a varied, beautiful, and resource-rich planet for future generations". Environmental sensitivity is a key entry-level variable in Hungerford and Volk's (1990) model of responsible environmental citizenship. As Chawla (1998:370) notes, Hungerford and Volk said that environmental sensitivity was "a 'prerequisite', or at the very least a variable 'that would enhance a person's decision-making', when environmental actions are taken".

Tanner was not alone in thinking like this, or in wondering about where such sensitivity came from or how it might be encouraged. Tanner reasoned that if "a major goal of environmental education is the production of an active and informed citizenry, environmental educators should know the kind of learning experiences that produce such persons".[4]

He was stimulated to carry out his research by his reading of the biographies and autobiographies of prominent conservationists. In these, he found numerous references to time spent either alone or with friends, in (usually) pristine environments. From this he wondered whether these had been significant experiences for the individual in their subsequent career choice.

He concluded from this that "an obvious technique is to examine retrospectively the lives of citizens who have demonstrated amply their informed and responsible activism" (Tanner 1980:20), and noted that the environmental education research literature did not contain accounts of such studies. He decided to investigate this by asking staff and officers of leading national conservation organisations in the USA about their backgrounds. Using an open-ended survey, he asked individuals to identify any formative influences on them which led them to choose conservation work.

His core finding was that childhood experience in the outdoors was the most reported factor in developing a personal concern for the environment.[5] Some 78% of his respondents (n=45) mentioned what Tanner summarised as "natural areas", and 58% mentioned what he summarised as "habitat", noting that "a majority of these influences first occurred during childhood or adolescence". He was alert to the possibility that the identification of the salience of natural areas in his study might well reflect the fact that all his research subjects were members of organisations focused on the preservation of wilderness and wildlife.[6]

As Louise Chawla (1998) notes in some detail, Tanner's paper inspired much further research. Some of this was by means of open-ended surveys like his own; others were by interview and questionnaire studies. Most were qualitative studies of autobiographical recollection and memory. Prominent amongst the researchers were Chawla herself, Joy Palmer in the UK, who drew on her work with the UK's National Association for Environmental Education, and Palmer's research collaborators across Europe.

Tanner reported (1980:23) that no one cited negative environmental experiences in their responses to his research. As Chawla noted (1998), this was in marked contrast to Palmer who introduced a category of disasters/negative issues which acted as stimulants. Chawla (1998:374) noted that Palmer (1993:27) speculated that:

> between the late 1970s, when Tanner conducted his research, and the late 1980s, when she did hers, there may have been "a marked increase in the influence of negative factors on individual thought and action" ... In addition, her category of miscellaneous responses included negative reactions to living in a town or concrete jungle (nine respondents) and worries about health effects of environmental problems (seven respondents): arguably answers that could be grouped under "negative issues".

This difference shows just how far significant life experience (SLE) research had evolved in 15 years: from a US study of conservationists, where their personal direct experiences of the wild were reported, to a British study of environmental educators, where their fears and apprehensions emerged. It was around this time that the remark quoted at the head of this chapter was made: "If we can identify the most significant life experiences to have, we can ensure that everyone has them."[7] This was heard with some incredulity, and challenged over its deterministic assumptions.

But was this anything new? Wordsworth himself wrote: "One impulse from a vernal wood / May teach you more of man, / Of moral evil and of good, / Than all the sages can."[8] But the key word here is *may*. Wordsworth did not write will, and he reinforced his use of may in the last line of the poem: "Come forth, and bring with you a heart / That watches and receives."

That significant learning experiences become clear in well-constructed retrospective research studies on a specialist population, is one thing. To expect the process to operate in reverse is to confuse it with medical interventions. For example, finding that people in areas where the water is rich in fluoride tend to have healthier teeth can justify a public health programme to add fluoride to the public water supply. But this only works because fluoride acts on the teeth; significant life experiences work (or don't work) in the mind. This is not to say that people should not be helped to have such experiences as they can be inherently educational; it's just that we cannot expect them always to have significant life-changing outcomes for everyone.[9]

Notes

1 Comment made at a UK Council for Environmental Education conference in the mid-1990s by a leading SLE researcher.
2 "Poem of The Child That Went Forth, and Always Goes Forth, Forever and Forever". See: tinyurl.com/y6jwmf3k at the Walt Whitman Archive.
3 Tanner's quotation differs from the text held in the Archive. This reads: "There was a child went forth every day, / And the first object he looked upon *and received with wonder, pity, love, or dread,* that object he became". The italic text was omitted by Tanner for some reason, and this is still missing from some online versions of the poem.
4 As, for example, set out in the IUCN definition (1970), the Belgrade Charter (1976), UNESCO's *Trends in Environmental Education* (1977), and the Tbilisi Declaration (1978).
5 ERIC summarises the research thus: "Professional staff and/or chapter officers of four citizen conservation groups were asked to describe those experiences most significant in the founding and development of their conservation interests. Youthful experiences in the outdoors and in relatively pristine environments were cited by 44 or 45 respondents." See: tinyurl.com/yyomnthy
6 82% of Tanner's sample were men as were 78% of Peterson's. This probably simply reflects the membership of such organisations at the time.
7 This is not a verbatim quote; although heard by one of the authors, his contemporaneous note has long-since been composted.
8 "The Tables Turned." See The Poetry Foundation at: tinyurl.com/y6xcywmo
9 Such criticism was one of the factors that led to a special issue of *Environmental Education Research* in 1999 which focused on significant life experience research. We also explore these issues in our chapter on John Muir.

Further reading

Chawla, L. (1998). Significant Life Experiences Revisited: A Review of Research on Sources of Environmental Sensitivity. *Environmental Education Research*, 4 (4), 369–382.
Chawla, L. (2001). Significant Life Experiences Revisited Once Again: Response to Vol. 5 (4) 'Five Critical Commentaries on Significant Life Experience Research in Environmental Education', *Environmental Education Research*, 7 (4), 451–461.

Environmental Education Research. (1999). Five Critical Commentaries on Significant Life Experience Research in Environmental Education. *Environmental Education Research*, 5 (4).

Hungerford, H. & Volk, T. (1990). Changing learner behavior through environmental education. *Journal of Environmental Education*, 21 (3), 8–21.

Palmer, J.A. (1993). Development of concern for the environment and formative experiences of educators. *Journal of Environmental Education*, 24 (3), 26–30.

Petersen, J. (1982). *Developmental variables affecting environmental sensitivity in professional environmental educators*, unpublished master's thesis. Southern Illinois University at Carbondale.

Tanner, T. (1980). Significant Life Experiences: A New Research Area in Environmental Education. *Journal of Environmental Education*, 11 (4), 20–24.

33

FAITH, HOPE, CHARITY AND THE ECOLOGICAL CRISIS

"The current instability of the natural system of the earth – the external environment of human beings – is only a reflection of the instability and pain within humans."[1]

One of the risks of searching the internet for information is that of finding completely made-up answers. This is nicely illustrated by the response given to this question sent to Yahoo!: What is the Assisi Declaration? What was its purpose? And what did it say about Christianity?

For a number of years, Yahoo!'s "best answer" to this was from Ode to Harry, who wrote:

Thw assisi declaration was the document written by st francis of assisi to the cardinal of rome asking him to make christmas a holiday throughout all the regions where members of the catholic religion existed.[2]

Plausible, perhaps, but just not true.[3] Five years later came a more accurate summary:

The Assisi declaration refers to a statement made by major religions of the world ... outlining their own unique traditions and ways to care for nature.

In fact, in 1986, the World Wide Fund for Nature (WWF International), marked its 25th anniversary by inviting representatives of five world religions[4] to Assisi to explore how they could work together on environmental issues.[5] Prince Philip, President of WWF, summarised the result of the 1986 meeting like this:[6]

We came to Assisi to find vision and hope: vision to discover a new and caring relationship with the rest of the living world, and hope that the destruction of nature can be stopped before all is wasted and gone. ... I am convinced that secular conservation has learned to see the problems of the natural world from a different perspective, and I hope and believe that the spiritual leaders have learned that the natural world of creation cannot be saved without their active involvement. Neither can ever be the same again.

Sometime after this, in 1995, Prince Philip launched the Alliance of Religions and Conservation (ARC) to continue working with the five faith groups. By 2000 six more faiths had joined the Alliance, and the total is now 12.[7] As ARC notes, these faiths and their networks have a particular relationship with the natural world. The rationale for bringing them together is that they:

> have immense influence socially, educationally, politically and culturally both at national and local levels. This influence, combined with their spiritual insight and commitment makes them one of the most powerful agents for social change in civil society.

The ARC website[8] hosts statements by each of the 12 faiths, which outline the basics of each faith's history, beliefs and teachings on ecology. Here are a number of illustrative (though far from representative) examples of what the statements say:

> We are not masters of this Earth; it does not belong to us to do what we wish. It belongs to Allah and He has entrusted us with its safekeeping. Our function as vicegerents, Khalifahs of Allah, is only to oversee the trust. The khalifah is answerable for his/her actions, for the way in which he/she uses or abuses the trust of Allah. Islam teaches us that we have been created by Allah, that we will return to Allah for Judgement, and that we are accountable for our deeds as well as our omissions. The khalifah will have to render an account of how he treated the trust of Allah on the Day of Reckoning.
>
> The current instability of the natural system of the earth – the external environment of human beings – is only a reflection of the instability and pain within humans. The increasing barrenness of the earth's terrain is a reflection of the emptiness within humans. The solution to problems manifest in our world lies in prayer and in accepting God's ... will, order, and system. With an attitude of humility, and surrender to the Divine Spirit, conscientious human beings can seek to redress the current crises of the environment and of social justice. In the Sikh Way this is done through the guidance of the Guru, who is the Divine Master and messenger of God.
>
> The Jain tradition ... means reverence for life in every form including plants and animals. Jains practice the principle of compassion for all living beings ... at every step in daily life. Jainism is fundamentally a religion of ecology and has turned ecology into a religion. It has enabled Jains to create an environment-friendly value system and code of conduct. Because of the insistence on rationality in the Jain tradition, Jains are always ready and willing to look

positively and with enthusiasm upon environmental causes. In India and abroad, they are in the forefront of bringing greater awareness and putting into practice their cardinal principles on ecology.

> The encounter of God and man in nature is … conceived in Judaism as a seamless web with man as the leader and custodian of the natural world. … Now, when the whole world is in peril, … it is our Jewish responsibility to put the defence of the whole of nature at the very centre of our concern. And yet it must be said, in all truth, that this question of man's responsibility to the rest of creation cannot be defined by simply expressing our respect for all of nature. There is a tension at the centre of the Biblical tradition, embedded in the very story of creation itself, over the question of power and steward-ship. … Man lives, always, in tension between his power and the limits set by conscience.

In 2011, 25 years on, a second meeting was held in Assisi of all the faith groups, and ARC published *Faith and Conservation* (Palmer & Finlay) in 2013.[9] This is full of encouraging stories[10] of how the intervention of faith groups around the world has made a positive difference to the Earth. For example, the actions of the Maronite Church in Lebanon to protect an ancient forest, fish (and fishing) conservation by Muslim leaders in Misali, an island off Tanzania, the Sikh declaration of a Cycle of the Environment, the Buddhist protection of Nepal project, and the defeat of the brown plant hopper in Indonesia.[11]

This is a valuable collection, and any reading of it gives hope that where religious influence is strong then individuals, families and small communities might be expected to take heed and act accordingly, and many faiths have parables to encourage just that. And that hope might even be realistic were the environmental damage we see around us all the fault of individuals, family and community groups. However, it isn't, and, outwith theocracies, faith groups have little hold on action by governments, their agencies, corporations and other powerful groups which are jointly and severally responsible.

A key feature of many faiths' approach to the prevention of ecological damage is that people will need to answer for their actions when they meet their maker. However rigorous a process this turns out to be, it will likely be far too late for those left behind and those yet to come who will inherit the wind.[12]

Notes

1 A Sikh perspective on the ecological crisis humanity faces.
2 Spelling, punctuation, etc. as per the original. See: tinyurl.com/y2k5kv6t
3 Saint Francis of Assisi (1182–1226) founded the men's Franciscan Order, the women's Order of St Clare, and the lay Third Order of Saint Francis. He was described by Prince Philip as "the saint of ecology" even though the term ecology was only coined in 1866 by Haeckel. See the chapter on von Humboldt.
4 Buddhism, Christianity, Hinduism, Islam and Judaism.
5 Or, in a more secular vein, for the biosphere.

6 Religion and Nature Interfaith Ceremony (Gland, Switzerland: WWF International, 1986:42) Cited in Palmer and Finlay (2013).
7 The six additional faiths were: Baha'ism, Daoism, Jainism, Shintoism, Sikhism, and Zoroastrianism. In 2013 the Confucianists joined.
8 See: arcworld.org/arc_and_the_faiths.asp
9 This was an update of a 2003 World Bank publication.
10 For Palmer, stories are key to our worldviews. In *Dancing to Armageddon* (1992) he notes: "We all inhabit worlds shaped by stories [and] we are profoundly shaped and influenced by the stories we tell, by the stories that are told around us, by the stories we think are actually fact, and by stories that have shaped the very language, imagery, and terms we use today." See this article by Martin Burdman in the *Executive Intelligence Review* for a critical commentary on these (and some of Palmer's other) ideas: tinyurl.com/y2nofj2s
11 There is a less convincing story of the use of Daoist philosophy to prevent the hunting of tigers for their bones and penises.
12 Proverbs 11.29. See: tinyurl.com/vfaebch
13 Available at: tinyurl.com/y6ox3e4u

Further reading

Palmer, M. (1992). *Dancing to Armageddon*. London: Harper Collins.
Palmer, M. & Finlay, V. (2013). *Faith and Conservation; new approaches to religion and the environment*. Bath: ARC (Alliance of Religions and Conservation). [13]

34

THE EARTH CHARTER

"Recognise that peace is the wholeness created by right relationships with oneself, other persons, other cultures, other life, Earth, and the larger whole of which all are a part."[1]

The Earth Charter is an international declaration of fundamental values and principles that its supporters say are needed to build a just, sustainable, and peaceful society across our planet.[2]

This is its idealistic Preamble:

We stand at a critical moment in Earth's history, a time when humanity must choose its future. As the world becomes increasingly interdependent and fragile, the future at once holds great peril and great promise. To move forward we must recognise that in the midst of a magnificent diversity of cultures and life forms we are one human family and one Earth community with a common destiny. We must join together to bring forth a sustainable global society founded on respect for nature, universal human rights, economic justice, and a culture of peace. Towards this end, it is imperative that we, the peoples of Earth, declare our responsibility to one another, to the greater community of life, and to future generations.

Its four principles are:

1. Respect and Care for the Community of Life
2. Ecological Integrity
3. Social and Economic Justice
4. Democracy, Non-violence, and Peace

The key idea is that people should come together to create a sustainable world based on respecting nature, peaceful co-existence, and human rights and justice for all. In reality, this means governments coming together.

The idea of the Earth Charter was born in 1987 when the World Commission on Environment and Development (the Brundtland Commission) published *Our Common Future* and called for new norms that would guide the transition to sustainable development. Discussion about an Earth Charter took place in the lead-up to the Earth Summit in Rio de Janeiro in 1992, but the Rio Declaration was all that emerged. However, in 1994 Maurice Strong (who was Secretary-General of the Rio Earth Summit) founded the Earth Council, and Mikhail Gorbachev formed Green Cross International, and they then jointly, with the support from the Dutch Government, developed the Charter as a civil society initiative. It took six years before a final version was agreed in 2000.

Its supporters made a major effort to secure endorsement of the Charter by the World Summit on Sustainable Development in Johannesburg in 2002. During this, many government leaders and NGOs declared their support for the Earth Charter, but formal recognition of the Earth Charter by the United Nations was not secured. Eighteen years on this has still not happened.[3] Nor, perhaps, is it ever likely to happen now, as the UN has the Sustainable Development Goals (SDGs) to promote. The SDGs might be similar to the goals of the Earth Charter but they come with targets and now have global recognition as the means to pursue sustainable development.[4]

In our recent book, *The World We'll Leave Behind*, we argued that the Earth Charter could be seen as "the *Magna Carta* for our times", given that England's Great Charter of 1215 was also concerned with rights, responsibilities and justice. Some 800 years later, the influence and impact of *Magna Carta* are clear, although they are not yet universal. Will it take as long for the values embodied in the Earth Charter to become accepted – or will they never be universally embraced because of the contradictions they embody and the assumptions the Charter makes about the perfectibility of humanity?[5]

Notes

1 Earth Charter principle 16f. See: earthcharter.org/discover/the-earth-charter
2 The Earth Charter: earthcharter.org. You can download it (in 65 languages) here: tinyurl.com/y2eb4ctd
3 A timeline of the Charter's development can be seen here: tinyurl.com/y4ye76ab and details of what it sets out to do here: tinyurl.com/y52yyhfc
4 It also seems that the Sustainable Development Goal process will be better able to take positive technological and socio-economic change (such as shifts to zero-carbon and circular economies) in its stride than the Earth Charter.
5 Inevitably there will be both winners and losers as a sustainable future unfolds; losers, at least in their own minds and on their own terms, will not be happy at least in the short term. This is just as important as more objective measures of progress and success.

Further reading

Scott, W. & Vare, P. (2018). *The World We'll Leave Behind: grasping the sustainability challenge*. London: Routledge.

35

THE BEHAVIOUR OF MODELS

"... knowledge is a real, but relatively minor, factor in predicting whether ... the public ... will know about specific pro-environment behaviors ... let alone whether they will actually undertake such behaviors."[1]

The overall goal of the Decade for Education for Sustainable Development (UN, 2004) was to integrate the values inherent in sustainable development into all aspects of learning to encourage behaviour change and thus create a more sustainable future.[2]

Emphasising the need for human behaviour change was something that Decade supporters found hard to resist,[3] despite its uneasy fit with the earlier focus on values which we saw in our chapter, The road to Tbilisi. Hungerford and Volk (1990:302) had already asserted that the ultimate aim of education itself was "shaping human behavior", and they argued that responsible pro-environment (citizenship) behaviour could be developed through environmental education. The strategies are known, they said, and the tools are available. The challenge lay in our willingness to do things differently from before (Hungerford & Volk 1990:317).

This model says that if we can:

- create a curriculum that takes sustainability issues seriously
- provide enough information about ecological concepts and environmental inter-relationships
- provide carefully designed opportunities for learners to acquire environmental sensitivity and a sense of empowerment, and enable learners to acquire analytical and investigative skills, and citizenship action skills ...

... then their attitudes will shift, and then their behaviour will change.

This has been an influential model rooted in a scientific-realist view of the world. It posits the idea of responsible environmental behaviours, arising out of Ajzen and Fishbein's (1980) theory of planned behaviour. It brings together an understanding of scientific and ecological concepts, how these relate to our every-day lives, and the psychological influences on those lives.

However, a problem with this model lies in its separation of the desire to act from the social and economic context within which those acts will take place. Indeed, all the non-psychological and rather awkward socio-economic issues have been dumped into a box labelled "situational factors". Kollmuss and Agyeman (2002:248) noted that, "the question of what shapes pro-environ-mental behavior is such a complex one that it cannot be visualized through one single framework or diagram". It is also now clear (Marcinkowski & Reid 2019; Moss et al. 2016) that knowledge and understanding don't always or necessarily lead to the desired behaviour change, or indeed any change at all.[4] Moss *et al.* report that in their study biodiversity understanding was the least important variable of those that were significantly related to self-reported pro-conservation behaviour.

It is completely understandable why all this was criticised by critical realists and socially critical theorists (Robottom & Hart 1995) who opposed what they saw as a behaviourist emphasis[5] which failed to critique the socio-political circumstances within which all such behaviours were inevitably embedded. The socially critical theorists' alternative model, rooted in emancipatory action research (Fien 1993), sought to help teachers and students work towards social transformation in order to bolster social and ecological justice and through this reduce socio-economic dis-parities. This model sets out to effect societal rather than personal behaviour change and is focused on the economic forces that buffet, contort and direct our lives. Its focus is to help teachers and students analyse the values behind socially learned behaviour patterns. It sets out to show them how to resist such forces and work towards social transformation. As Huckle (2019) notes:

> To be critical [education] should reveal the structures and processes at work in the world that lead to injustice, a lack of democracy, and a failure to realise sustainable forms of development. It should reveal ideology that masks the structures and processes and should offer social alternatives or ways of realising justice, democracy, and sustainability that can empower individuals and com-munities as they apply theory to practice.

A key focus is helping students ask appropriate socially critical questions, typically of the *cui bono?* form.[6]

This model says that if we can:

- influence opinion-formers (e.g. teachers), and through them, learners
- raise their awareness and consciousness (and counter false consciousness) of the issues that prevent a sustainable society ...

... then their underpinning values will be changed, and they will argue, work, vote, demonstrate and agitate for (pro-sustainability) societal change.

This approach also criticised what it claimed to be liberal education's reluctance to ask critical questions of society because of its focus on the individual as a learner where education was, to a significant degree, seen as for itself with too little emphasis on behaviour change and social inequities.

The liberal educators' response was that encouraging critical, open-minded questions of society, and looking for the need for change, is its *raison d'être*, although answers are never pre-specified as they tend to be in socially critical and/ or behavioural approaches. Anyway, they argue, it's no business of any educator to persuade learners to change behaviours or society in pre-specified ways. Rather, this is a job for politicians, socio-political activists, social marketeers, newspapers, bloggers, business, and the advertising industry. Of course, this illustrates a potential liberal education blind spot, where its own preferred approach to education can be said to contribute towards the perpetuation of particular social models. Huckle (2013) considers these approaches in the context of ESD and Eco-Schools.

What seems common ground is that all these approaches can be seen as an education in citizenship: a responsive social learning process which is a preparation for informed, clear-headed, socio-political engagement with the main existential issues of the day that occur in the family, the community and workplace – that is, in all aspects of a lifelong learning. Clearly, being socially critical, and actively considering changes in entrenched behaviours, are each citizenly qualities that are necessary if societies are to actively re-create themselves, and a way has to be found to bring these together in an open-minded way in schools and other institutions if building an acceptable quality of life for all people is to be possible.

Schools, colleges and universities, as institutions, are an acknowledged, integral part of any learning society, with the key role of supporting young people in the early stages of their learning; that is, in their acquiring the wide-ranging under-standing, skills and capabilities that they will need to continue to develop for suc-cessful and fulfilling engagement with, and living in, the world. In this view, the purpose of schools, broadly speaking, might be to stimulate young people's devel-opment of awareness and interest in relation to living sustainably, with the hope (but not certainty) that this will give rise to social participation that contribute, for example, to the goals of greater social justice and human well-being, and the bol-stering of the resilience of ecological systems. As Jensen and Schnack (1997) have argued, it is not about developing citizens who will behave in particular and pre-determined ways.[7]

Notes

1 Moss et al. (2016). Available at: tinyurl.com/s35ht4o
2 Not everyone, of course, thought that such values (often described as neo-liberal) were particularly valuable.
3 This continued emphasis on individual behaviour change pervades thinking about the outcomes of ESD programmes. See, for example, Vare and Scott (2008) for a comment

on the tendency within global learning and development education programmes in schools to promote (as opposed to critically appraise) fair trade schemes.

4 Critics of this model didn't need such analytical studies to know that the relationship between knowledge and behaviour was much more complex that the model assumed.

5 It was never really accurate to describe this as behaviour*ist* although it was always a useful label to attach to rival ideas given how poorly actual behaviourist approaches within education are usually viewed.

6 That is: in whose interests is this being done?

7 This view, which is a classic liberal education stance, is rejected by many contemporary advocates of curriculum reform for whom the whole purpose of reform is to prescribe behaviours that will militate against future climate change and mitigate the problems it currently causes. See also Scott (2016).

Further reading

Ajzen, I. & Fishbein, M. (1980). *Understanding Attitudes and Predicting Social Behaviour*. Eaglewood Cliffs, NJ: Prentice Hall.

Bronner, E.B. (2011). *Critical Theory, a very short introduction*. Oxford: Oxford University Press.

Fien, J. (1993). *Education for the Environment: critical curriculum theorizing and environmental education*. Geelong: Deakin University Press.

Huckle, J. (2013). Eco-schooling and sustainability citizenship: exploring issues raised by corporate sponsorship. *The Curriculum Journal*, 24 (2), 206–223.

Huckle, J. (2019). Powerful geographical knowledge is critical knowledge underpinned by critical realism. *International Research in Geographical and Environmental Education*, 28 (1), 70–84.

Hungerford, H.R. & Volk, T.L. (1990). Changing learner behavior through environmental education. *Journal of Environmental Education*, 21, 8–21.

Jensen, B.B. & Schnack, K. (1997). The Action Competence Approach in Environmental Education. *Environmental Education Research*, 3 (2), 163–178.

Kollmuss, A. & Agyeman, J. (2002). Mind the gap: Why do people act environmentally and what are the barriers to pro-environmental behavior? *Environmental Education Research*, 8 (3), 241–259.

Marcinkowski, T. & Reid, A. (2019). Reviews of Research on the Attitude-Behavior Relationship and their Implications for Future Environmental Education Research. *Environmental Education Research*, 25 (4), 459–471.

Moss, A., Jensen, E. & Gusset, M. (2016). Probing the Link between Biodiversity-Related Knowledge and Self-Reported Proconservation Behavior in a Global Survey of Zoo Visitors. *Conservation Letters*, 10 (1), 33–40.

Robottom, I. & Hart, P. (1995). Behaviourist EE Research: Environmentalism as Individualism. *Journal of Environmental Education*, 26 (2), 5–9.

Schultz, P.W. (2011). Conservation means behaviour. *Conservation Biology*, 25, 1080–1083.

Scott, W. (2016). *ESD as Transformation – a liberal review*. Thematic Essay for Routledge's Sustainability Hub. Web link: tinyurl.com/weaxodh

United Nations (UN). (2006). *UNESCO Framework for the UN DESD International Implementation Scheme*. New York, NY: United Nations. Web link: tinyurl.com/u8pmky4

Vare, P. & Scott, W. (2008). *Education for Sustainable Development: two sides and an edge*. London: Development Education Association. Web link: tinyurl.com/y5v8ckvu

36

THE COMING OF ESD

"Two adjectival educations (environmental education and development education) should be seen as integral to sustainable development education."[1]

The idea of education for sustainable development (ESD) emerged through successive iterations in international meetings and documents. An early cross-over point occurs in *Caring for the Earth: a strategy for sustainable living* (IUCN, UNEP & WWF 1991:54–55), which calls for more environmental education and a meeting of "*the training needs for a sustainable society*". The document also aligns environmental concerns with humanist goals such as universal primary education, a view that appears to assume, uncritically, that education is *a part of* sustainable development. However, at this stage, this was a fairly loose allocation of labels with ESD not yet being a widely used term.

This had changed by the time of the World Summit for Sustainable Development in Johannesburg in 2002, where the term ESD became widely used. *Agenda 21*, a key output of the 1992 Earth Summit in Rio de Janeiro, suggests that two adjectival educations (*environmental education* and *development education*) should be seen as integral to "sustainable development education" (Keating 1993). Subsequently, the UN's Millennium Development Goals (MDGs), agreed by world leaders in 2000 and covering issues such as poverty, child mortality, gender inequality and environmental degradation, became core ESD concerns.[2] Following the World Summit, with ESD established as an idea, the Japanese government led the proposal for a United Nations Decade of Education for Sustainable Development (DESD), to begin in 2005. Ahead of this date, another UN body, the Economic Commission for Europe (UNECE) was charged with piloting a regional Strategy for ESD under its *Environment for Europe* process. Thus, even as the concept was evolving and still struggling for recognition at national levels, ESD had acquired considerable international momentum.

Against the apparent success of the ESD brand, in UN circles at least, it remained labelled as an education package, and unfortunately, like environmental education before it, one that was "comparable with and separable from many other educational packages" (Smyth 1995:4). And yet, it was clear, even then, that if ESD were to make a serious contribution to resolving or managing the interconnected crises facing humanity, it would need to become part of the fabric of education systems, even if that meant that it had, itself, to disappear as a distinctive aspect of education to do so. The problem with this calculus is two-fold: firstly, the system itself is not amenable to change, and secondly, many of ESD's own promoters are reluctant to see it becoming absorbed into the mainstream, because of the loss of their ownership and influence that this entails.[3] In the defence of environmental education and ESD, as Sterling (2010:216) notes, labels are important because they carry meaning for practitioners – though not necessarily for policy makers, who have competing interests and priorities to address.

Sterling also highlights this tension between inclusivity, as promoted by the UNDESD,[4] and the "fragmentation where various education-for-change emphases assert their distinctiveness". And he is not the first to note the argumentation that takes place within the field about the relationships between the various adjectival educations. For example, questions such as the following remain important for many promoters of EE and/or ESD:

- Is environmental education now synonymous with ESD?
- Is ESD a component of environmental education, or environmental education a component of ESD?
- Has environmental education evolved into ESD?
- Does the advent of ESD mean environmental education is outmoded?
- Is development education (and global learning) within or outside ESD?
- How does climate change education fit in here?

... and so on. Meanwhile, policy makers, and those responsible for national curriculum structures, get on with shaping education to more mainstream (and often economic and instrumental) ends.

Despite its early promise, UN parentage, and high-level patronage, ESD has struggled to gain wide acceptance within formal education systems, partly through a lack of clarity, possibly through a tendency to proselytise, and certainly through its misalignment with current educational priorities which, as we note elsewhere, remain economy-focused, and PISA-influenced,[5] especially in rich societies.

One of the problems with ESD is that, because of its UN-style jargon and its transformative nature (Jackson 2011; Sterling 2010), it is replete with insider meaning but with little by way of outreach to people not steeped in that way of thinking, and its core meanings and possibilities are hard to articulate. As a consequence, much of what takes place in schools in the name of ESD has been limited by wider policy parameters. One result of this is that it is often necessary to simplify the message to the point of completely diffusing it in order to get it across to busy professionals already heavily engaged with other priority aspects of government policy. For example, in the early 2000s in England, the then Labour Government's (in very many ways) admirable[6] sustainable schools initiative communicated the essence of ESD to schools by referencing it to its own recent policy initiatives around child welfare, saving energy, sustainable transport, waste, and international development.[7] In making these links with the *parts* of (E)SD, through an accommodatory stance, the essence of the *whole* was lost, except in those few schools which already understood what was at stake and the need for change in relation to leadership, values and vision. Because of this, ESD's cutting edge was blunted as, because the world is radically interconnected, anything less than a systemic view of the issue in hand tends to be woefully inadequate.

What, then, might be viable alternatives? Perhaps one of the most distinctive proposals is Sterling's (2001) outline of "sustainable education" underpinned by an ecological paradigm, something that calls for a wholesale seeking of transformation in education rather than attempting to tinker around the edges of the system. However, rather like the Bible, ecology itself offers a wide range of potential "lessons" which one can select in order to reflect one's own worldview or vision of social order. From nature we can be inspired by the power of cooperation; we can also insist on the importance of competition. Further, just as the UK government's Sustainable Development Education Panel (SDEP 1998) used sustainable development principles, rather inappropriately, to describe what it called education for sustainability (i.e. ESD), it would be equally inappropriate to use ecological principles to underpin ESD – fundamentally this is about the human learning process, ecology *per se* is not.

A number of other attempts have been made to explore the idea of ESD and clarify ways of thinking about it. One such is the idea of ESD 1 and ESD 2 (Vare & Scott 2007). In this, ESD 1 (learning *for* sustainable development) promotes "positive" behaviours where the need is identified and agreed. ESD 2 (learning *as* sustainable development) aims to build capacity to think critically about expert advice, exploring the contradictions inherent in trying to do the "right" thing. Crucially, ESD 1 and ESD 2 are not seen as two separate approaches, rather they are complementary sides of the same coin, and ESD 2 makes ESD 1 meaningful because our long-term well-being depends both on current actions *and* our capability to question critically and assess alternatives.

Notes

1 Quoted from Agenda 21 by Keating (1993).
2 Another early appearance was, ironically enough, something of a polemic against ESD in Jickling's much-cited 1992 article.
3 This pincer movement, unarticulated though it is, represents a formidable barrier to change, and it is a phenomenon seen within many of the interests and activities that seek to change the education system whilst being reluctant to change themselves.
4 Though not always by UN agencies where turf wars are common, for example, between proponents of ESD and Education for All (EFA).

5 PISA is the Organisation for Economic Co-operation and Development (OECD) Programme for International Student Assessment: tinyurl.com/53x42
6 See Reynolds and Scott (2011) for a critical perspective on this.
7 No other country's experience, reported so far (for example, see the reports of the International Alliance of Leading Education Institutes: intlalliance.org), seems to have overcome this core problem.

Further reading

IUCN, UNEP & WWF. (1991). *Caring for the Earth: A Strategy for Sustainable Living.* Gland, Switzerland: IUCN, UNEP and WWF.

Jackson, M.G. (2011). The Real Challenge of ESD. *Journal of Education for Sustainable Development,* 5 (1), 27–37.

Jickling, B. (1992). Why I don't want my Children to be Educated for Sustainable Development. *Journal of Environmental Education,* 23 (4), 5–8.

Keating, M. (1993). *The Earth Summit's Agenda for Change: a plain language version of Agenda 21 and the other Rio agreements.* Geneva: The Centre for Our Common Future.

Reynolds, J. & Scott, W. (2011). Sustainable Schools in England: background and lessons learned. In *2011 Annual Journal and Review.* London: National Association of Field Studies Officers.

SDEP. (1998). *Education for Sustainable Development in the Schools Sector: a report to DfEE/ QCA.* Reading: Council for Environmental Education.

Smyth, J. (1995). Environment and Education: a view from a changing scene. *Environmental Education Research,* 1 (1), 1–20.

Sterling, S. (2001). *Sustainable Education, Re-visioning Learning and Change.* Dartington: Green Books.

Sterling, S. (2010). Living in the Earth: Towards an Education for Our Time. *Journal of Education for Sustainable Development,* 4, 213.

Vare, P. & Scott, W. (2007). Learning for a Change: exploring the relationship between education and sustainable development. *Journal of Education for Sustainable Development,* 1 (2), 191–198.

37

GREEN STILL DOES NOT ALWAYS MEAN GO

"White people, all we want is to join you at the dinner table and eat with you. If you do not want us to sit with you at the table, then we have no choice but to destroy the table."[1]

In 1995, Nelleke Bak, of the University of the Western Cape, published a paper which discussed in a nuanced way a range of attitudes in South Africa to the widely assumed notions that environmental education was (i) a good thing, and (ii) needed to be implemented urgently and widely.

Bak argued that these two assumptions could not be taken for granted in South Africa, because of its particular history of apartheid and consequent developmental needs. She set out four responses to what she saw as a dominant Western/Northern interpretation of environmental education and argued that one particular response might prove the most fruitful to pursue, as the country developed economically and socially and moved beyond tensions generated by race and class issues.

Response A rejected both assumptions. Its supporters, Bak said, argued that redressing the imbalances created through apartheid through increasing access to economic, educational and social resources, and through providing housing and health facilities, were much more important than implementing objectives concerned with the conservation of natural resources. A just society implied that those who have suffered hardships should be adequately compensated, both economically and materially, for their past sacrifices. Crucially, this group saw that the message of most environmental education, "with its call for a decrease in unnecessary consumption, may be interpreted as just another 'hidden' form of apartheid, in the sense that it tries to thwart the acquisition of (entitled) material goods".

Response B accepted that environmental education is a good thing because of its message that we have a moral responsibility to care for the environment in order to ensure the survival of future generations. However, it rejected the notion that it was urgent. Its supporters understood the long-term desirability of conservation and environmental education but argued that financial resource should be channelled most urgently into housing, health care and economic development.

Response C accepted both assumptions, but Bak said that such views tended to come from within those groups who were most economically secure; that is, the population of European heritage.

Response D also accepted both assumptions, but with conditions. Its supporters recognised the need to involve local communities in decision-making drawing on their needs, traditions and knowledge. They said that the justification for caring for the environment was not just about human physical survival, but about the sacredness and inherent worth of nature itself. This would, Bak said, be an environmental education "interpreted in the light of the traditional conservation ethic, embodied in African myth and ritual". It was this approach that she thought might prove the most fruitful to pursue.[2]

It was clear at the time that this range of views was not restricted to South Africa, despite its unique suffering because of apartheid. However, such views were mainly found in countries whose economies were also still developing and/or had a history of colonial exploitation.

Twenty-five years on from the end of apartheid nothing much has changed in terms of wealth and power distribution, despite a new constitution and a fully enfranchised adult population; the vast majority of the dispossessed then, remain so now. However, the nature of the discourse has changed from environmental education and conservation to climate change, the sustainable development goals, and to the Paris Agreement which set up an international legal framework for countries to shift toward a zero-carbon world.[3]

So how well do these four responses work for the situation we now face with climate change? To explore this question, it's necessary to change the original assumptions to something like this:

> Assumptions: [i] combating climate change is a good thing; [ii] it needs to be done urgently and globally.

Given that 189 countries[4] have now ratified the Paris Agreement, a superficial conclusion would be that all have accepted both assumptions (Response C, above). In reality, however, for many countries, it means that they have accepted the first assumption but have reservations concerning the timetable for action (Response B). Indeed, they were encouraged to do this by the Paris Agreement process. Many countries argued that they would cut carbon emissions in time but only after their economy developed some more and caught up with those countries which had had a head start. For example, India made that argument. When pressed about the ethics of this, given the state of the planet, the Indian government pointed to the advantages that other countries had had historically in being able to emit carbon with no thought of tomorrow.[5] The UK is one such country,[6] of course, and the fact that the UK was the previous colonial power in India, added weight to their argument.[7]

Prior to the Paris Agreement coming into effect, countries publicly outlined what post-2020 climate actions they intended to take: these were their Intended Nationally Determined Contributions (INDCs).[8]

The following statements are taken from the South African INDC:[9]

> South Africa is committed to addressing climate change based on science and equity.
>
> South Africa's national response considers both development needs and climate change imperatives.
>
> South Africa is committed to cooperative efforts to adapt to the unavoidable adverse impacts of climate change.
>
> The nature of the climate change challenge is one characterised by the overuse of a global commons in an unequal world.
>
> Given that poor countries and communities have the least responsibility for the challenge of global climate change but are the most vulnerable to its impacts, adaptation to the adverse effects of climate change is also a global responsibility and concern.
>
> South Africa faces the challenge of climate change as a developing country, with overriding priorities to eliminate poverty and eradicate inequality. [This] requires addressing major challenges in creating decent employment, which in turn requires sustainable economic development, improving basic education, health and social welfare and many other basic needs such as access to food, shelter and modern energy services.
>
> South Africa is presently facing acute energy challenges that hamper economic development. As a result of the historical development pathway of its energy sector, South Africa is currently heavily dependent on coal, with a fleet of old and inefficient coal-fired power plants that are nearing, but not yet at, the end of their design life-cycles …
>
> … in the short-term (up to 2025), South Africa faces significant rigidity in its economy and any policy-driven transition to a low carbon and climate resilient society must take into account and emphasise its overriding priority to address poverty and inequality.

This is a clearly a Response B position, although it begs the question about how long the shift to Response C should take. In other words, in making the shift to a net-zero carbon economy, how urgent is urgent?; how long should it take? This rather Augustinian[10] question is not confined to South Africa as it applies to all countries that have ratified the Paris Agreement and is an issue we explore in other chapters.

Notes

1 Julius Malema, leader of South Africa's Economic Freedom Party, speaking at an election rally in Soweto on May 6, 2019.

2 A fifth possible, but illogical, view is that it was urgent but not necessary.

3 We're not aware if Nelleke Bak has updated her paper.

4 The Agreement has been signed by 195 countries and ratified by 189 (March 2020 figures). These represent some 90% of global emissions. See: tinyurl.com/ybq8fjlf

5 India's Paris Agreement pledge is a 33% to 35% reduction in the emissions intensity of its gross domestic product (GDP) by 2030 compared to the 2005 level.

6 It is easy to over-egg this pudding. Although the UK's 2019 proportion of carbon emissions is only around 1% of the global total, it has been emitting since the start of the Industrial Revolution. However, when these cumulative historical emissions of CO_2 are taken into account some 2–3% of human-induced global warming to date has resulted from UK greenhouse gas emissions. See: tinyurl.com/yyqqoed9 page 20.

7 India's INDC promises a 33% to 35% reduction in the emissions intensity of its GDP by 2030 compared to 2005 levels.

8 INDCs are converted into NDCs as the nature of the contribution is determined by the country. The World Resources Institute (WRI) explains this process here: tinyurl.com/y5sgq85p. The WRI's INDC tracker is here: tinyurl.com/y43ct4o5

9 South Africa's greenhouse gas reduction target is that emissions will be in a range between 398 and 614 tonnes of CO_2 (equivalent) by 2025 and 2030. CO_2 equivalent figures include all greenhouse gases and not just carbon dioxide itself. South Africa's INDC can be found here: tinyurl.com/y6y7zenc

10 St Augustine wrote: "Grant me chastity and continency, but not yet." *Confessions*, XIII, chapter 7, 17. For the full text see: tinyurl.com/y5c3avc8

Further reading

Bak, N. (1995). Green Doesn't Always Mean "Go": Possible Tensions in the Desirability and Implementation of Environmental Education. *Environmental Education Research*, 1 (3), 345–352.

UK Committee on Climate Change. (2019). *Net Zero – The UK's contribution to stopping global warming*. Web link: tinyurl.com/yyamge6c

UN. (2015). *The Paris Agreement*. UN Climate Change. Web link: tinyurl.com/ybq8fjlf

World Resources Institute. (2019). *Intended Nationally Determined Contributions*. Web link: tinyurl.com/y5sgq85p

38

THE BEGINNING OF THE END, OR THE END OF THE BEGINNING?

"We've spent 30 years baking tempting desserts of fun and frivolous activities, but forgot an even more important skill: how to cook the main course."[1]

In 1998, Doug Knapp[2] and then John Smyth[3] published short op-eds in NAAEE's *Environmental Communicator*.[4]

The stimulus for Knapp's article was the publication of the Thessaloniki Declaration in 1997. This was the product of the United Nations conference that celebrated the 20th anniversary of the 1977 Tbilisi Declaration and the fifth anniversary of the 1992 Rio Earth Summit. It was attended by over 1,000 delegates and its prime purpose was to adopt a declaration that set out education strategies to enable the goals set out in Chapter 36 of Agenda 21 to be realised.[5]

Knapp (1998:12) wrote: "The culmination of this UNESCO-sponsored event was ... a charter on the future of education for sustainability [which] may be noted as the beginning of the end for environmental education." He added (p. 12): "environmental education is virtually non-existent in the declaration. The term is only used once in the 14 recommendations to promote sustainability."

The thrust of this opening section was clear: environmental education had lost out in competition with those advocating a broader focus on sustainability. It had been, in Knapp's terms, "swallowed by another fashionable approach".[6] Implicit in this view was that a focus on the imperilled biosphere had been (at best) diluted.

Knapp then outlined what he saw as three issues that "aided in environmental education's poor showing" at the Thessaloniki conference and in the declaration. He made it clear that he felt that these had little to do with the strength of any pro-sustainability argument. The issues were:

[i] an activity guide mentality:

> "For the most part, environmental educators have taken the easy way out ... [which] has negated the use of more substantial models that encourage ... long-term thinking and responsible citizenship on the part of the students."

[ii] the promotion of activism at the expense of action:

> "Far too many see our field as a way to preach their own agendas rather than as an accountable educational process that can educate and empower"; and

[iii] a lack of appropriate training.

> The true essence of environmental education is the development of autonomous thinkers who are capable of making responsible decisions ... Training for this depth of education is time-consuming and unfortunately scarce.

If only environmental educators had not lost their way (or their collective soul), Doug Knapp's implicit argument seemed to be; if only they'd focused on educating teachers rather than producing glossy resources and projects, then the outcomes of Thessaloniki would have been different. This is, however, hard to believe as the tides of sustainability and sustainable development were already running hard.

Knapp's piece must have captured the disquiet felt by at least some environmental educators at how international agreements were shifting the focus to sustainability away from the problems that nature faced because of increased human interaction and exploitation, and the pressures of population and economic growth. He ended his article (ibid.:14) by, firstly, re-stating the need for "environmentally literate and responsible citizens" who will be able to "make decisions that will help check many of the environmental problems that will arise in the 21st century"; and then by setting out a number of strategies that would make environmental education more effective. At the heart of these was the proper training of schoolteachers.

John Smyth's response to the Knapp article was an understanding one which sought some common ground. He agreed, for example, with the criticisms of environmental educators that Knapp had set out. However, Smyth's key response was that the well-being of people and the health of the biosphere were intimately linked and that a focus on one needed a reciprocal focus on the other to make it realistic. He noted that this was not a new view but had been set out by the World Conservation Strategy in 1980, adding correctly that "the definitions of environmental education generated at Belgrade and Tbilisi (UNESCO, 1977) were comprehensive enough to take in people, culture, sustainable development and all" (Smyth 1998:14). This was, of course, a criticism of those environmental educators who preferred a focus on nature rather than on anything more rounded.

Smyth (p.14) then cautioned environmental educators against opting out of the newly emerging international consensus, urging them to "keep within the system" as otherwise "their influence on education may dwindle away". Not everyone took notice. In the 20 or so years since Thessaloniki this divide remained in that education for sustainable development and global learning initiatives treated the environment as a secondary issue, and environmental educators mostly let them do this.

However, there are now new factors. One is the Paris Agreement with its international recognition of the need to address climate change (even if responses to the problems remain limited and inadequate). Another is the adoption of the 17 Sustainable Development Goals which bring environment and development matters together as never before. A third is the now-widespread acceptance of the serious issues we face because of global heating and its effect on biospheric cycles and systems and the climate. This has shifted the ground, with even traditional environmental educators seeing a role for what they do. A fourth is the keen involvement of young people causing their voices to be heard both on the streets and in their schools. It will be harder for both governments and environmental educators to ignore this new phenomenon.

Notes

1　Doug Knapp quotes this in his article. It was written by Michael Weilbacher who, in a critique of contemporary US environmental education, went on to say: "We've spent 30 years inventing supplemental field trips and activities. So what's the meat and potatoes? … we must walk into the front doors of schools armed with carefully constructed curricula featuring focused, sequential, knowledge-based programs."
2　Knapp was a faculty member of the Department of Recreation and Park Administration at the University of Indiana Bloomingdale. See: tinyurl.com/ub76eqo
3　Smyth was the pre-eminent British environmental educator of his generation.
4　Knapp expanded on his argument in a *Journal of Environmental Education* article in 2000.
5　Agenda 21 was an outcome of the Rio Earth Summit. Its prime objective was that local governments should draw their own local Agenda 21. Chapter 36 dealt with education.
6　Just as, Knapp asserted, conservation and outdoor education had previously "succumbed to the more politically correct term of environmental education".

Further reading

Knapp, D.H. (1998). The Thessaloniki Declaration – the beginning of the end for environmental education? *Environmental Communicator*, 28 (2), 12–14.

Knapp. D.H. (2000). The Thessaloniki Declaration: A Wake-Up Call for Environmental Education? *Journal of Environmental Education*, 31 (3), 32–39.

Smyth, J. (1998). Environmental education – the beginning of the end or the end of the beginning. *Environmental Communicator*, 28 (4), 14–15. Reprinted (Chapter 80) in Reid, A. & Dillon, J. (2016). *Environmental Education*. London: Routledge.

UNESCO. (1977). *International Conference on Environmental Education, Tbilisi, USSR. Final Report*. Paris: UNESCO.

39

IN COMPETENCE WE TRUST

"Competence is no longer a scarce commodity."[1]

Anyone with a passing interest in environmental and/or sustainability education will have noticed how, for over two decades, there has been much talk of competences, whether these are core competences for sustainability or focused specifically on education for sustainable development. This reflects a wider trend in education that we might call the competence turn.

The language of competences in education shifts the focus away from inputs (what is taught), to outputs (what is learned). This is production line thinking, or curriculum as product, that plans education around what the learner should be able to do, what they should know, even who they should be, as a result of their learning. It fits with the rise of managerialism in education since the 1980s. To some extent this made a lot of sense, particularly in the UK where competence statements underpinned the development of National Vocational Qualifications (NVQs) in areas as diverse as chainsaw handling and managing care homes. It does, however, reflect a Newtonian logic that views processes as predictable and manageable, which rather flies in the face of our understanding of the world and the social processes within it as interacting complex, adaptive systems.

An early example in relation to environmental learning is the set of competencies prepared for the International Environmental Education Programme (IEEP) (Wilke et al. 1987), discussed in Chapter 31. You will notice that this talks of competency (and competencies) rather than competence (or competences); a difference that demands some explanation. In discussing the development of NVQs in the UK, Terry Hyland (1994) makes a clear distinction between competence and competency. The former is seen as the broader term often meaning a capacity to fulfil a certain role or procedure, whereas competency is narrower and refers to a specific skill or ability. That said, the IEEP authors, being from the USA, may well have seen competency as the broader term as distinct from "learning outcome" that for them would be more specific. Competency was also used by the OECD, the organisation behind the Programme of International Student Assessment (PISA), when in 1997 it launched the Definition and Selection of Competencies (DeSeCo) Project. This set out to define competencies necessary for individuals to confront the challenges of balancing economic growth with environmental sustainability and social equity.

By 2005, when the United Nations Economic Commission for Europe (UNECE) published its Strategy for Education for Sustainable Development (ESD), the preferred term was compe*tence* and a key area for action within the Strategy was to "develop the competence within the education sector to engage in ESD" (UNECE 2009:21).[2] In an attempt to meet this call, the international organisation ENSI (Environment and School Initiatives) developed the CSCT model (Curriculum, Sustainable development, Competences, Teacher training).[3] This provided a dynamic, complex framework of competences that simultaneously recognised teachers as individuals, members of professional networks and citizens within wider society. This captured a complex picture but also made the model challenging to implement. Just as the ENSI project was nearing completion, UNECE itself convened an "expert group" to define its own set of ESD competences for educators. This led to the development of 39 competences gathered under three broad headings: (a) holistic approach; (b) envisioning change; (c) achieving transformation.

While the ENSI and UNECE models provided a useful insight into the range of competences that an educator of ESD might need, neither model was readily adaptable to already compressed teacher education programmes. It was frustration with this situation that led to a more recent attempt to define an accessible set of educator competences through a European Union-funded project called *A Rounder Sense of Purpose* (RSP), involving institutions from nine countries coordinated in the UK by the University of Gloucestershire. RSP defines 12 competence areas arranged under the same three headings of the UNECE framework; whether these are truly competences is debatable, as will become apparent.[4]

The common understanding of "competence" can mean a minimum level of skill, as distinct from mastery, or it can denote a valued level of accomplishment, as in a competent surgeon. It can also be seen as a quality that one develops gradually (or loses) over time. This lack of shared understanding suggests that the term is poorly theorised, which in turn leads to difficulties in assessing competence. How do we know, for example, whether a lecturer is competent? Do we look at whether their students go on to find gainful employment, something for which a lecturer can claim only partial credit, however competent they are, or is it enough to establish that they can prepare material with an appropriate level of difficulty, an activity that can be broken down into measurable skills and knowledge?

In the case of the RSP project it was decided not to break the 12 competence areas down into skills, values, knowledge, etc., in order to facilitate assessment. This was because such an approach atomises learning into discrete components that can appear meaningless and actually undermines the notion of holistic thinking that is central to sustainable development. This atomising tendency was recognised by Wim Westera, who, in attempting to differentiate skills from competences for purposes of assessment, recognised that:

> we should also acknowledge that skills themselves can also be decomposed into a hierarchical system of sub-skills. Consequently, the entanglement of the skills-hierarchy and the competence-hierarchy produces a complex, confusing and inconsistent conceptual system that cannot be taken seriously. (Westera 2010:85)

At the time of writing, work continues apace on defining and assessing competences for ESD with research teams active in many countries. Meanwhile the RSP project is side-stepping the whole notion of measurement, deciding instead to focus on quality criteria.[5] While the RSP project uses the language of competences, the title of the project signifies a broader intent, i.e. reframing the purpose of education in order to embrace wider concerns beyond its current economic focus. This represents a deliberate challenge to the whole notion of reducing education to sets of competences; whether it succeeds in shifting the thinking in this area remains to be seen.

Notes

1 The quote is from Godin (2012:16). Seth Godin claims that given our general level of competence, it's time to break away from this production line model and treat our work as art in order to better connect with others.
2 The UNECE competences are outlined in *Learning for the Future: Competences in Education for Sustainable Development*, available at: tinyurl.com/y5jgdttm
3 The CSCT framework is available at: tinyurl.com/tcnwywt
4 *A Rounder Sense of Purpose* competence framework and related materials, including activities that use the competences to teach about the UN Sustainable Development Goals, are available at: tinyurl.com/s3drnvy
5 This approach reflects that taken in the past by ENSI, see: Breiting et al. (2005).

Further reading

Breiting, S., Mayer, M. & Morgensen, F. (2005). *Quality Criteria for ESD-Schools: Guidelines to enhance the quality of Education for Sustainable Development*. Vienna: ENSI/SEED & Austrian Federal Ministry of Education, Science & Culture. Web link: tinyurl.com/qlhe6aw

Godin, S. (2012). *The Icarus Deception: How High Will You Fly?* London: Penguin.

Hyland, T. (1994). *Competence, Education and NVQs: Dissenting perspectives*. London: Cassell Education.

UNECE. (2009). *Learning from each other: The UNECE Strategy for Education for Sustainable Development*. Geneva: United Nations.

Westera, W. (2010). Competences in education: a confusion of tongues. *Journal of Curriculum Studies*, 33 (1), 73–88.

Wilke, R.J., Peyton, R.B. & Hungerford, H.R. (1987). *Strategies for the training of teachers in environmental education*. International Environmental Education Programme; environmental education series No. 25. Paris: UNESCO-UNEP.

40

ENVIRONMENTAL LEARNING

"Practitioners in EE typically continue to talk past one another, rather than with one another."[1]

This book is concerned with environment and learning, and it is tempting to run these words together as environmental learning. For many, this conflation has an immediate though potentially misleading appeal because it can be seen to apply to the outcomes of environmental education. It is misleading in two possible senses: (i) it implies that such learning is always an outcome of environmental education, whereas this is not inevitable; and (ii) it can lead the unwary to assume that environmental education (or even teachers) are needed for environmental learning to take place, whereas this has never been the case. A third problem with the phrase, which is also a considerable strength, is its permissive breadth and studied vagueness which we might term a loose framing (Scott 2015; Scott & Vare 2018: chapter 34).

An early use of the phrase in the literature was by Scott and Gough (2003) in an *Environmental Communicator* article about the various interests that they had observed amongst the many delegates attending the annual conferences of the North American Association for Environmental Education (NAAEE).[2] The prime purpose of the article was to identify the range of learning foci arising from human encounters with the environment that they had seen represented at these conferences over time. Acknowledging the third problem noted above, the authors defined environmental learning purposefully loosely as "learning which accrues, or is derived, from an engagement with the environment or with environmental ideas".[3]

In this article, Scott and Gough identified nine categories of interest that capture a range of foci and objectives of those who espouse and promote such learning (Table 1).

TABLE 1 Scott and Gough's nine categories of interest

Categories of interest	Focus/outcomes
1 those **interested in sharing the joy and fulfilment derived from nature**, in order to bring about significant life-enhancing and life-changing experience for learners	**Nature** values & feelings
2 those **interested in the study of the processes of nature** in order to understand, or to teach about them	**Nature** understanding
3 those **using nature as an heuristic** to foster the development of knowledge, understanding, skills and character which, although situated, are transferable to other contexts and through time	**Nature** skills
4 those **using the natural and/or built environments as heuristics** to achieve conservation and/or sustainability goals	**Conservation** understanding
5 those **advocating/promoting individual behaviour changes** in order to achieve conservation and/or sustainability goals	**Conservation** behaviours
6 those **advocating/promoting particular modes of social change** in order to achieve environmental and/or conservation/sustainability goals	**Social Change** social justice
7 those **using environmental, conservation and/or sustainability issues as contexts** for the development of skills and knowledge related to the exercise of democratic social change	**Social Change** democratic citizenship skills
8 those **promoting nature as a metaphor for a preferred social order** – which may be "cooperative" or "competitive", according to worldview	**Social Change** values
9 those **interested in the study of environmental learning** (and environmental education) itself	**Learning** learning about learning

They argued that what the categories had in common is that engagement with the environment, one way or another, can give rise to learning. In setting these categories out, Scott and Gough differentiated between the interests in terms of their foci and their value base, and offered examples of each. For instance, for Category 1, they wrote:

> non-formal educators and interpreters seeking attitudinal and/or value change; possibly seeking to introduce and extend particular philosophies of living.

In their analysis, they showed how emphasis varied across interests and illustrated how those interested in environmental learning can have widely differing assumptions about both purpose and process.

Whilst it is tempting to argue that such a categorisation provides evidence for how multi-disciplinary environmental education (and cognate disciplines) are, it would be a specious claim. As Disinger (1983/1977:30) noted:

> though EE is ideally interdisciplinary – an eclectic assemblage of interacting disciplines – its practitioners typically approach it as if it were

multidisciplinary – an eclectic assemblage of discrete disciplines. Because EE's practitioners typically are grounded in no more than one of the multiplicity of disciplines involved, logic leads them to approach EE through the intellectual filters of their own disciplines. Thus, practitioners in EE typically continue to talk past one another, rather than with one another.

All too often, that still seems the case today.

But can this loose framing of environmental learning be justified? We suggest that whilst it is defendable up to a point, it is surely too wide-ranging to be comprehensively applicable. Specifically, we think that this loose view of environmental learning holds good until we shift from a focus on environment (or nature) to a consideration of sustainability/sustainable development when its limitations and limits become apparent, as the following example illustrates.

In 2007, the Higher Education Funding Council for England (HEFCE)[4] commissioned the Policy Studies Institute (PSI), a think tank, to undertake a strategic review of sustainable development in higher education in England. The main aim of the review was to establish a baseline of activity related to sustainable development across the sector, against which to measure progress and publicise what the sector is already doing. A crucial issue in this review was what is to count, for survey purposes, as "activity related to sustainable development". For the purpose of the review, such activity was defined by the research team as activity that contained:

> a significant element related to either or both of the natural environment and natural resources, PLUS a significant element related to either or both of economic or social issues.

For example, a study of the Earth's climate system would only count if it considered socio-economic aspects or impacts of climate change – that is, if it considered people and their interests. Fundamentally, not even a study of the changing climate system would count unless it did this.

Viewed against that exacting but appropriate standard, it is only Scott and Gough's Categories 4 to 7 that should count, though not everyone can be expected to agree with this, just as researchers in universities refused to be constrained by the PSI definition in reporting what they did.

Notes

1 See Disinger (1983/1977).
2 The NAAEE conferences draw those interested in environmental learning from a broad range of interests including, research, evaluation, school teaching (kindergarten to Grade 12), college and university programmes, the not-for-profit sectors, international NGOs, government (local, state and national), business, think tanks – and more. In addition, NAAEE covers Mexico, Canada as well as the United States.

3 Scott and Gough argued that such learning could be the outcome of formal or non-formal educational programmes in schools, and/or communities, from designated environmental education interventions, or from personal or incidental learning where no teacher was involved.
4 HEFCE (2007). See: tinyurl.com/tmze8yz

Further reading

Clearinghouse for Science, Mathematics and Environmental Education. (1983). *Information Bulletin*, 2. Web link: cnr.uidaho.edu/css487/EE_Definitional_Problem.pdf

Disinger, J.F. (1983/1977). Environmental Education's Definitional Problem. *ERIC Clearinghouse for Science, Mathematics and Environmental Education Information Bulletin*, 2. Web link: tinyurl.com/yybls7pc

HEFCE. (2007). *HEFCE strategic review of sustainable development in higher education in England.* London: Higher Education Funding Council.

Scott, W. (2015). Exploring a transformative orientation to sustainability in universities: a question of loose and tight framings. *Environmental Education Research*, 21 (6), 943–953.

Scott, W. & Gough, S.R. (2003). Using the environment as a stimulus to learning: exploring categories of interest. *Environmental Communicator*, 33 (1), 8.

Scott, W. & Vare, P. (2018). *The World We'll Leave Behind*. London: Routledge/Greenleaf.

41

EXTINCTION? REBELLION?

"You can't be a little bit sustainable. Either you are sustainable or you're not sustainable."[1]

The Extinction Rebellion (XR)[2] movement was formed in the UK in late 2018. Its aim is to use non-violent civil disobedience to achieve radical change in order to minimise the risk of human extinction and ecological collapse. The initial rebellion was against the UK government and what XR sees as its inadequate climate change policies, but now the scope is international.

XR's favoured tactic is to disrupt aspects of normal life so thoroughly that the arguments are rehearsed through the prolonged national publicity that is achieved. For example, in November 2018 five major bridges across the Thames were blocked, trees were planted in Parliament Square, and a coffin representing our future was buried there. Bridge blocking was repeated in April 2019, along with the occupation of the Oxford Street shopping artery, but this time far more people were involved and it was the top item on nightly television news. The weather was perfect, there was a party atmosphere, celebs[3] and personalities came along to get in on the action – and the disruption was considerable.[4]

XR has three demands of the UK government:

1. tell the truth by declaring a climate and ecological emergency, working with other institutions to communicate the urgency for change
2. act now to halt biodiversity loss and reduce greenhouse gas emissions to net zero by 2025
3. create and be led by the decisions of a Citizens' Assembly on climate and ecological justice

This is not so much a challenge to government, as to culture, and the scale of the change that is sought is shown in XR's principles and values, which include:

- Break down hierarchies of power for more equitable participation
- Leave comfort zones to take action for change
- Follow a cycle of action, reflection, learning, and planning for more action
- Create a culture which is healthy, resilient and adaptable

As the aim to "reduce greenhouse gas emissions to net zero by 2025" shows, it is also a challenge to the economy. The current UK government policy was set in 2008 and promises an 80% reduction in carbon emissions by 2050. This could well be achievable, but doing so by 2025 has implications for infrastructure, economy and individuals. *The Times* interviewed Gail Bradbrook, co-founder of XR, who acknowledged that decarbonising means replacing 26 million gas boilers used for home heating.[5] Bradbrook asked, rhetorically, why it wouldn't be possible to replace these by electric ones by 2025 and compared the task to building 400 aircraft in six weeks during World War II. "We will pull it off if we believe in ourselves", she was reported as saying.[6]

This recourse to a wartime spirit of coming together in the face of an existential threat is a popular strategy by those wishing to encourage difficult change, but it is a hard sell some 80 years after the event when for 95% of the population, there is no memory of the war.[7]

Another difficulty is that not everyone is convinced that the issues XR are warning against are existential. XR knows this, and so confronts the public with that reality in a hard-hitting way in order to create public acceptance for the necessary sacrifice to enable what they term "a world that is fit for generations to come".

It is, however, uncertain whether XR is serious about the 2025 deadline. It would, after all, also mean shutting all the gas-fired power stations as well (as there is no working carbon capture and storage system in place). So where is all the electricity to come from (by 2025) to run these boilers on cloudy, windless days when, typically, some 40% of electricity comes from carbon-based fuels? It could be, therefore, that the 2025 date is meant to shock into wakefulness rather than being a fixed policy objective. That is, it's not the date that really matters, but the idea. Either way, XR runs the risk of seeming to be either unrealistic in its aims or uncaring about the hardships that millions would likely face.

Many have asked why the UK has been singled out for criticism as it has in some ways a relatively good decarbonising story to tell, and only contributes less than 2% of global emissions anyway.[8] Go and tell the Indians, and try sitting down in Tiananmen Square and see where it gets you, were typical responses from inconvenienced and exasperated people in London.[9]

The UK story is a good one, comparatively, in part because other countries' efforts have been so poor. The UK has, for example, made good progress at decarbonising electricity production, has the largest number of electric vehicles in

Europe, has a strong commitment in law to overseas aid (some of which is targeted at carbon-reduction strategies), and its CO_2 emissions keep falling. But the official carbon data tend to exclude some high-carbon factors such as shipping and aviation, not to mention all the carbon that is externalised to those countries from whom we now import manufactured materials and goods.[10]

Greta Thunberg told members of the UK Parliament that the UK had run up a "mind-blowing historical carbon debt" over the past 200 years, with the implication that the UK needs to account and atone for that legacy in tangible ways. One of these might be the sort of rapid decarbonisation that XR is advocating, as this would set an example to the world. Another might be through significant financial transfers to countries that are still developing economically in order to help defray decarbonising costs. Or both. So, if the UK voluntarily impoverishes and immiserates itself, will that be sufficient penance? Or can such an egregious sin never be expurgated, and a special place in Hell awaits the country that kick-started the Industrial Revolution?[11]

All this will be a hard sell to voters who might know that they are well-off comparatively, but do not feel so in any absolute sense. Asking people (and their children) to forego a piece of the better life they were promised so that others far away whom they will never know can have a better life themselves will likely always prove difficult when *real* sacrifices have to be made. It will test values and religious ethics. However, the debate has shifted with climate change. Now, the idea of a better life for everyone is under threat in an absolute sense and not a comparative one.

As politics is always the art of the possible, it could be that the seriousness of the message gets acted on, but not in an urgent way.[12] Ironically, as policy inevitably feels its way forward in this unprecedented arena, this might be the approach that best accords with the precautionary principle.

Notes

1 Swedish teenage climate activist, Greta Thunberg, speaking to *The Times* on April 23, 2019.
2 See: rebellion.earth
3 Some celebrities, it seems, flew in just for the event.
4 During the XR occupation of London over 1,000 people were arrested but only 69 were charged.
5 Billen (2019).
6 The target means that the internal combustion engine would need to be phased out and commercial flying halted, in the absence of carbon capture and storage systems.
7 We expect to see similar entreaties based on the community "COVID spirit", which at the time of writing in early 2020 appears to be a phenomenon in the making.
8 It is only as low as this if you discount the country's imports, especially of carbon-heavy materials such as steel or aluminium.
9 Global CO_2 emissions rose by 2.7% in 2018 to 37.1 billion tonnes (a record figure). In the UK, they fell by 2%, the lowest figure since 1888 (except for 1893, 1921, and 1926 when there was large-scale industrial unrest).
10 Speaking in Parliament on April 23, 2019, Greta Thunberg described the UK's two-faced approach to carbon in which it approved of fracking for shale gas, expanded

airports and approved a new coal mine as "beyond absurd". On the same day, a government minister noted that since 1990 the UK's carbon emissions have fallen by 40% while the economy has grown by two-thirds. "Prosperity and green policies are not incompatible", he said.

11 Such reparations are suggested in the 2025 report from the Centre for Alternative Technology (CAT 2019), although no figures are set out. One of us estimates that the UK is responsible for ~5% of the entire CO_2 production since the Industrial Revolution. See: tinyurl.com/vunopnz

12 We explore this issue in our chapter, Green still does not always mean go.

Further reading

Billen, Andrew. (2019). Extinction Rebellion founder Gail Bradbrook: "We're making people's lives miserable but they are talking about the issues". *The Times*, April 19. Web link: tinyurl.com/ybgn6l3g

Centre for Alternative Technology (CAT). (2019). *Can we Reach Zero Carbon by 2025?* Machynlleth: Centre for Alternative Technology. Web link: cat.org.uk/can-we-reach-zero-carbon-by-2025.

PART III
Future possible

42

BEHIND THE CENES

What stories shall we tell?

"The earth is full of refugees, human and not, without refuge."[1]

The stories that we choose to tell ourselves about nature are crucial in determining our relationship with the natural world. Since the Enlightenment we have been moving away from religious or supernatural interpretations of natural phenomena in favour of a scientific understanding based on analyses of components of nature largely in isolation from ourselves. So, when we learn that geology, a venerable member of the Earth Sciences, is poised to declare a new geological epoch, the *Anthropocene* (the epoch defined by human actions), it rather changes the conversation. We can no longer pretend that there are natural sciences and then there are social sciences; instead we must re-think our disciplinary boundaries. Indeed, such boundaries can be seen as a fundamental part of the problem.

Firstly, we should understand how this proposed geological re-framing fits within our view of the Earth's long history. Geologists divide the Earth's 4.6 billion years into nested units of time.

- The largest of these are Eons. There have been two of them: the Precambrian and the Phanerzoic.
- Eons are subdivided into five Eras. The Cenozoic is the current one.
- Eras are subdivided into Periods. We are now in the Quarternary.
- Periods are subdivided into Epochs. The Holocene ("completely recent") is current.
- Epochs are subdivided into Ages. The Holocene has been subdivided into three: the Greenlandian, the Northgrippian and, most recently, the Meghalayan.

To summarise what is a complex picture: we are living in the Meghalayan Age of the Holocene Epoch of the Quarternary Period of the Cenozoic Era of the Phanerzoic Eon.[2]

These were confirmed by the International Commission on Stratigraphy as recently as July 2018.[3] Each subdivision in the geological record is pinpointed by a distinctive, globally traceable marker in the record often related to changes in life-forms or climatic shifts showing up in the fossil record. These markers are known colloquially as golden spikes.[4]

The Holocene is deemed to have begun at the end of the last ice age, some 11,700 years ago, and the Holocene golden spike is defined using ice cores from the North Greenland Ice Core Project (NGRIP) in central Greenland.

The idea of the epoch re-framing (Holocene to Anthropocene) was first proposed in 2000 by the atmospheric chemist and Nobel laureate Paul Crutzen. Since then the concept has generated a fair degree of controversy. What scientists do agree upon is that during the latter part of the 20th century we have witnessed "the most rapid transformation of the human relationship with the natural world in the history of humankind" (Steffen et al. 2015:131). Potential golden spikes for the Anthropocene have been proposed as the nuclear weapons use in the 1940s, climate change, biodiversity loss, and ozone depletion.

Over Earth history, a shift to the Anthropocene would be unique because, as far as we can tell, it would be the first to be driven by a single species (us), and even more unusually, we would know that we are doing it. This opens up an array of choices, of opportunities as well as threats, all of which demand a vast amount of learning, something which is central to the theme of this book.

Not everyone is happy about the use of the term Anthropocene, however. One charge is that this is just typical human hubris: naming geology after ourselves. Another is that as not all humans are responsible, it seems wrong to blame the entire species.

Andreas Malm and Jason Moore suggest that Capitalocene would be a more accurate description. Moore (2016) argues that, after agriculture, the big shift in altering the world was the moving of plant material around the globe through exploration and colonisation.[5] Later industrialisation was also largely driven by capitalism and, while few would deny that very many humans now live a longer and generally more materially comfortable life, the benefits of capitalism are yet to be fully shared across the human species.

Donna Haraway agrees and is sceptical of the term Anthropocene because of the inseparability of organisms and their environments. In a 2015 paper, she argues:

> No species, not even our own arrogant one pretending to be good individuals in so-called modern Western scripts, acts alone; assemblages of organic species and of abiotic actors make history, the evolutionary kind and the other kinds too. (Haraway 2015:159)

Haraway says that decisions about terminology (Anthropocene/Capitalocene/etc.) must reflect scale, rate, synchronicity, and complexity, and that the question has to be, when do changes of degree become changes of kind? She quotes Anna Tsing (2015), who suggests that the inflection point between the Holocene and the Anthropocene might be the wiping out of most of the refugia[6] from which diverse species assemblages (with or without people) can be reconstituted. Tsing argues that the Holocene was the long period when such places of refuge still existed to sustain re-worlding in rich cultural and biological diversity. Haraway's preferred term, Chthulucene, is derived from "chthon" (Greek for "earth") and a spider, *Pimoa cthulu*, that lives under redwood stumps in California. The significance of the spider is its multiple limbs; the essence of the Chthulucene is that it has many tentacles of possibility. There is no neat rounding off in this story.

Haraway explains that more than one name is warranted because:

> we need a name for the dynamic ongoing sym-chthonic forces and powers of which people are a part, within which ongoingness is at stake. Maybe, but only maybe, and only with intense commitment and collaborative work and play with other terrans, flourishing for rich multispecies assemblages that include people will be possible. I am calling all this the Chthulucene – past, present, and to come. (Haraway 2015:160)

Scott Gilbert has proposed[7] that the Holocene–Anthropocene re-framing might not just be a shift of epochs, but a boundary event, comparable to the boundary between the Cretaceous and the Paleogene Periods (the K–Pg boundary).[8] This is quite a suggestion as this K–Pg boundary was a sudden mass extinction of some three-quarters of the plant and animal species on Earth, which took place about 66 million years ago because of an asteroid strike. With the exception of species such as the leatherback sea turtle and crocodiles, no tetrapods weighing more than 25 kilograms survived. It marked the end of the Cretaceous Period and with it, the entire Mesozoic Era opening up the Cenozoic Era which continues today.

Despite the claims that another mass extinction is actually taking place, many might think this a premature judgement, especially as all the refugia have not yet been wiped out and very many species remain, despite the stories that some tell. As we noted at the outset, the stories that we choose to tell ourselves about nature are crucial in determining our relationship with the natural world; too much gloom surely inhibits our learning as well as our willingness and ability to make a better future possible.

Notes

1 Donna Haraway (2015:160).
2 For simplicity this assumes that the Holocene–Anthropocene shift has not yet happened.
3 International Commission on Stratigraphy. (2018). Web links: tinyurl.com/qlw6pma and tinyurl.com/vz9xcgo
4 More formally, they are termed Global Boundary Stratotype Section and Point (GSSP).
5 See, for example, the role of Kew Gardens in the development of the rubber industry by the movement of seeds from Brazil to South-East Asia. This story is well told in Henry

Hobhouse's *Seeds of Wealth* (2005). Hobhouse's book, *Forces of Change* (1989), has considerable detail on the spread of plants round the world. The role of the slave trade and the establishment of plantations is an unambiguously wicked part of this story. So much so that Plantationocene has also been suggested as an alternative term.

6 This is defined by Merriam Webster as an area of relatively unaltered climate that is inhabited by plants and animals during a period of continental climatic change (such as a glaciation) and remains as a centre of relict forms from which a new dispersion and speciation may take place after climatic readjustment.

7 Quoted by Donna Haraway. See: tinyurl.com/rra8n96

8 K stands for Kreide (German for chalk), the traditional abbreviation for the Cretaceous Period, and Pg is short for the Paleogene Period. The boundary between these two periods takes physical form and can be seen in many exposed rocks across the globe. See Geology Page at tinyurl.com/urjdnty

9 Paper given at The Anthropocene Conference: Arts of Living on a Damaged Planet, May 2014, Santa Cruz, CA. Videos and more information are available here: tinyurl.com/sscnq2n

Further reading

Haraway, D.J. (2014). Anthropocene, Capitalocene, Plantationocene, Chthulucene: Staying with the Trouble. In *Acts of Living on a Damaged Planet*. May 9. Santa Cruz Vimeo, Inc.[9]

Haraway, D.J. (2015). Anthropocene, Capitalocene, Plantationocene, Chthulucene: Making Kin. *Environmental Humanities*, 6, 159–165.

Hobhouse, H. (2004). *Seeds of Wealth: four plants that made men rich*. London: Pan Books.

Hobhouse, H. (1989/2005). *Forces of Change: an unorthodox view of history*. Berkeley, CA: Shoemaker & Hoard.

Moore, J.W. (Ed.). (2016). *Anthropocene or Capitalocene? Nature, History and the Crisis of Capitalism*. Oakland, CA: PM Press.

Steffen, W., Sanderson, A., Tyson, P.D., Jager, J., Matson, P.M., Moore, BIII, Oldfield, F., Richardson, K., Schnellnhuber, H.J., Turner, B.L.II & Wasson, R.J. (2004). *Global change and the Earth system: a planet under pressure*. New York, NY: Springer-Verlag.

Tsing, A. (2015). *Feral Biologies*. Paper for Anthropological Visions of Sustainable Futures, University College London, February 2015.

43

BEING HUMAN

"... the ship had sent a request on a postcard to the BBC's World Service, asking for 'Mr David Bowie's "Space Oddity" for the good ship *Arbitrary* and all who sail in her.'"[1]

This final chapter considers where the relationship between nature and learning might be leading us in future and the extent to which it can contribute to our having a future at all.

The launch of the *Sputnik 1* satellite was probably the most celebrated event of the 1957–1958 International Geophysical Year. As we embarked on the space race it seemed that technology was leading us away from our home planet altogether. Yet space travel helped us to appreciate the fragility of Earth, famously photographed from *Apollo 8*, seemingly suspended in infinite space.[2] As *Apollo 17* astronaut Eugene Cernan remarked, we went to explore the Moon, and in fact discovered the Earth.

Indeed, the International Geophysical Year helped us to understand nature on a whole new scale. Among its landmark achievements was the granting of funds to a bright young chemist called Charles Keeling to help establish an observatory on Hawaii's Mauna Loa volcano. At an altitude of 3,397 metres in the mid-Pacific, the site was considered ideal for measuring global atmospheric trends far removed from pollution sources. Early readings showed annual fluctuations in atmospheric carbon levels, something Keeling realised was due to plant growth in the northern hemisphere absorbing CO_2 in the summer and releasing it in winter. In subsequent years measurements showed how atmospheric CO_2 concentrations were increasing annually. Over decades these readings charted a sharply rising line, now known as the "Keeling Curve". Regardless of opinion on global warming and the role of fossil fuels, the Mauna Loa readings are clear – and they do not bode well for humanity. We return to this below.

In recent decades a different kind of space race has been taking place, building ever-expanding functionality into objects of ever-decreasing size. From satellite navigation to digital music to drone warfare, digitisation and miniaturisation appear to be supplanting the bulky analogue world. As our shrinking machines get smarter, we seem to be bracing ourselves for the full impact of artificial intelligence (AI). Perhaps this is the point at which we finally leave nature behind, although some fear we may be left behind ourselves in the process. The late physicist Stephen Hawking was certainly wary when he declared that, "we cannot know if we will be infinitely helped by AI, or ignored by it and side-lined, or conceivably destroyed by it".[3] That said, the fact that we sense inherent risks in creating intelligences that surpass our own suggests that we will endeavour to design these dangers out of the system, aided in no small part by an awareness of the darker side of our own complex human nature.[4]

What is natural and what is technological may become an impossible distinction if we step beyond augmenting our own bodies with implants that send and receive data, to actually modifying the human genome so that our descendants are born with technologically enhanced characteristics. This could be seen as the ultimate break with nature yet isn't this a continuation of our distinctively human characteristic of sharing language and thought down the generations? In this way we would literally become the embodiment of Guattari's three ecologies.[5]

Before any of this takes place, however, nature itself may yet be our undoing, possibly in the form of a global pandemic facilitated by the deep interconnectedness of the modern world. Again, our best defence lies in thinking ahead, not for a specific threat but for the likely traits that would allow a global pandemic to take hold. In 2017 a group of leading scientists[6] met at the Johns Hopkins Center for Health Security in Baltimore to discuss the characteristics of micro-organisms that would constitute a global catastrophic biological risk. They identified key traits that such pathogens would likely have:

- efficient human-to-human transmissibility (i.e. an airborne, respiratory disease)
- the ability to transmit during incubation periods
- an appreciable fatality rate – but not too high lest the pathogen runs out of hosts
- not been exposed to many people hitherto so that levels of natural immunity are low and there is no readily available cure[7]

In this case our expanding knowledge of nature in the form of sophisticated biotechnology and advanced planning could help us to side-step a potential source of mass annihilation.

Another enduring threat from nature is the possibility of an asteroid strike large enough to shroud the planet in dust and destroy our ability to grow food, or even to dislodge the Earth from its orbit altogether. With this in mind, NASA and the European Space Agency are working on scenarios in which humanity has only a few months' warning of such an event. Once again, a preparedness combined with advanced technology is being marshalled to protect us. Plans include redirecting asteroids using combinations of robotic craft, nuclear warheads and solar-powered super-lasers. NASA's DART mission (Double Asteroid Redirection Test),[8] scheduled to take place in 2021/2022, will (or *did*, depending on when you read this) attempt to deflect the non-threatening Didymos asteroid by slamming a rocket into its moon at a speed of 6 km per second. It's thought that this should be enough to make a tiny adjustment to the moon's orbit which, over hundreds of thousands of kilometres, will change the course of the larger body.

With this wealth of technology at our disposal, we could be lulled into a warm sense of our own invincibility, but the threats we are facing this century are perhaps even more complex than these single-source, natural phenomena. The alarming loss of biodiversity – the rich variety of living things – is a human-induced catastrophe amounting to the sixth mass extinction in the long history of life on Earth. Causes are complex but the trend started with the arrival of agriculture with its wholesale destruction of natural habitats. Problems are compounded by the use of agrochemicals and increased urbanisation, although climate change will soon become the leading cause.[9]

All of which brings us back to the world's longest record of atmospheric CO_2 measurements at the Mauna Loa Observatory. Advisers on the Intergovernmental Panel on Climate Change estimate that concentrations of atmospheric CO_2 should not exceed 430 parts per million (ppm) in order to achieve the Paris Agreement's target of limiting global temperature increase to 1.5° Celsius above pre-industrial levels. In 2015 400ppm was reached; by July 2019 it was almost 412ppm and rising.[10] At this rate the 430ppm limit will be breached before 2030 and possibly sooner given that environmental trends tend to be non-linear. This non-linearity is because feedback mechanisms within nature's complex systems can magnify impacts. A familiar example of positive (or reinforcing) feedback is the melting of the Arctic's permafrost resulting in massive releases of methane, a gas 30 times more potent at trapping the sun's heat than CO_2. Such mechanisms confound our calculations. The warm air that sparked a European heatwave in July 2019 moved on to Greenland where it caused a rapid and unprecedented increase in surface melting affecting approximately 90% of the surface of the ice sheet. Earlier climate models had predicted this level of melting would occur in 2070.[11]

Given the various threats that nature poses, climate change is undoubtedly the most immediate. In a widely read academic paper of 2018,[12] Professor Jem Bendell outlined a strong case for assuming that societal collapse is imminent in the near future. As if remarking on the theme of this book, Bendell suggests that: "climate change is not just a pollution problem, but an indicator of how our human psyche and culture became divorced from our natural habitat".

Perhaps such a "divorce" was inevitable. In our opening chapter we observed how humans live in a dual reality: the objective reality of our physical world and a constructed reality of our imaginations. If a near-term societal collapse is as inevitable as Bendell suggests, then it will be the stories that we choose to tell ourselves, with education having a central role in conveying these, that may yet determine our survival.

We would do well not to allow our darker nature, that which we would like to design out of AI, to dominate. Drawing on our basic instincts, we could choose to recognise each other as a resource, our best hope for survival, or as a threat to our own existence. Assuming we manage to side-step the worst of the phenomena outlined above, we may learn our way forward to adapt to an ever-changing environment or learn to adapt the environment more effectively to our own purposes. We will probably do both because, being human, we are uniquely gifted with that choice.

Notes

1 Extract from the Iain M. Banks novella, *The State of the Art* (1989/1993:149) in which the Culture spaceship, *Arbitrary*, sits invisibly above the Earth monitoring what is going on. Debate rages over whether to leave us alone to our self-destructive ways, to intervene to help us sort ourselves out, or whether the whole "incontestably neurotic and clinically insane species" should be consigned to a black hole. The ship's AI (which was really in charge) at least has a sense of humour.
2 Far from being suspended, the Earth travels round the Sun at an average speed of ~30 kilometres per second (km/sec.). The solar system, meanwhile, travels round the centre of the galaxy at ~230 km/sec. The galaxy is also moving quickly, relatively speaking.
3 Report on Stephen Hawking speech: tinyurl.com/y7oywttd. There is already a considerable literature on the post-Human world.
4 The exploration of artificial intelligence and human morality can be dated at least as far back as Mary Shelley's *Frankenstein* while Isaac Asimov's 1950 science fiction thriller *I, Robot* informs the ethics of artificial intelligence to this day.
5 For the detail of Guattari's three ecologies, see: tinyurl.com/vpdb54l
6 *The Characteristics of Pandemic Pathogens*: tinyurl.com/y35c2n84
7 As we finalise this chapter in March 2020, the latest pandemic to hit us is a coronavirus, COVID-19. This meets all four of these criteria, with a fatality rate that appears (at the time of writing) to be about seven times that of seasonal influenza (0.7 v. 0.1). Being a novel virus it is more dangerous than flu because there is no reservoir of human immunity. The latest World Health Organization reports can be seen at: tinyurl.com/u4upd62
8 NASA's DART Mission: tinyurl.com/yaor6bxj
9 "Wildlife crisis worse than economic crisis." IUCN press release (July 2009): tinyurl.com/kk7tld
10 For the latest Mauna Loa CO_2 data visit: tinyurl.com/yauwoncs
11 News of Greenland ice melt is here: tinyurl.com/y6zho44g and tinyurl.com/y4j3zxtg
12 Bendell (2018). Available at: tinyurl.com/y3bpmqq8

Further reading

Bendell, J. (2018). *Deep Adaptation: A Map for Navigating Climate Tragedy*. Occasional Paper 2, Institute for Leadership and Sustainability (IFLAS). Lancaster: University of Cumbria.

APPENDIX 1

A brief history of environment and learning in England

Although environmental education is popularly thought of as beginning in the mid-1960s, learning focused on the environment in a broad sense has a much longer history. In this chapter we present a timeline sketch of some of the significant developments and influences, and notable contributors in the nation we know best: England.

In England, environmental educators tend to say that there have been four major strands to its development: an environmental/nature studies tradition, a conservation tradition, an outdoor education tradition, and an urban studies tradition. But this is an insider perspective. Viewed from without, that is against a backdrop of long-term socio-economic change, things look rather different.

What we see are (i) a range of political and other initiatives that are, in most part, a reaction to social and other problems caused by the economic development of the country through the Industrial Revolution in particular, and urban growth more generally; (ii) a broad social movement to protect the countryside from over-development; and (iii) a growth of scientific interest in a systematic study of the natural world. Broadly speaking, these represent a combination of public health and human well-being (both physical and mental) concerns with conservation and ecological interests. Over time, as Keith Wheeler (1975) notes, there were two significant developments: (i) a change of focus of interest in the countryside from its amenity value to the conservation of nature, and (ii) a move from seeing the study of nature as the key focus to the more political orientation and associated activism that environmental education offered. Our slowly growing understanding of the existential nature of the problems we face was a factor in these shifts.[1] Additionally, as Nick Jones has pointed out, whilst the focus of environmental education can be seen as the problems caused to the environment (the natural world) by people, the focus of urban studies, beginning with Patrick Geddes, can be seen as the problems caused to people by their environment (where they live and work). These different perspectives have now been brought together in the Sustainable Development Goals.[2]

Pre-1800

John Evelyn writes *Fumifugium* in 1661 in which he complains that London's "inhabitants breathe nothing but an impure and thick mist".

Gilbert White understood humanity's dependence on the biosphere and is now widely thought of as the country's first ecologist because of his close and systematic study of the natural world. He published *The Natural History and Antiquities of Selborne* in 1789.

1800s

Concern about nature as content, teacher and victim was the focus of a number of early 19th-century novels.[3] These themes were also found in biblical teaching and in the work of educationalists and the Romantic poets.[4]

As the 19th century progressed, and wind and water slowly gave way to steam as the source of motive power, the authorities struggled to deal with the growing problem of foul air, polluted water and terrible living conditions in the cities. Royal (and other) commissions were established and select parliamentary committees convened to no great effect. Although the Alkali Act of 1863, and its first Chief Inspector, **Angus Smith**, proved a pivotal point, it wasn't until the Clean Air Act of 1956 that lasting progress was made.[5]

William Wordsworth was the Romantic poet who railed against the overdevelopment of the countryside and argued through his poetry that nature could be a convincing teacher if only people paid attention. He was in many respects an environmentalist.

Archibald Geikie argued in an 1879 lecture to the Royal Geographical Society against the commercial exploitation of nature across Europe. With **Henry Huxley**, he promoted environmental studies for children, linking physical geography, science and outdoor activities.

Patrick Geddes was the first person credited with connecting the quality of the environment with the quality of education; he established urban environmental studies programmes in Edinburgh in the mid-1880s.

The **Society for the Protection of Birds** (SPB) was founded by Emily Williamson in Manchester in 1889 to stop the trade in feathers for women's hats which was devastating the populations of egret, bird of paradise and other species.

Nature study and gardening were, by the late 1890s, officially approved modes of study in elementary schools, with cross-curricular programmes of study connecting work inside and outside the school. These, Marsden (1997:13) says, were intended to "equip children with moral and spiritual insights".

Ebenezer Howard publishes *To-Morrow: a peaceful path to real reform*, in 1898. This describes a utopian city where people live harmoniously with nature. It led to the **Garden City Movement** and to the creation of the first garden city, Letchworth, in 1903.

The Garden Cities and Town Planning Association (now the Town & Country Planning Association – TCPA) was founded in 1899 by Ebenezer Howard to enhance the urban environment. It is the UK's oldest charity concerned with planning, housing and the environment.

1900–1940

The School Nature Study Exhibition was established alongside five conferences focused on the aims and scope of nature study, and the **School Nature Studies Union** was set up in 1903 in response to these.[6] Its motto was "To see and admire; not harm and destroy".

1905 Board of Education Regulations required elementary schools to provide observation lessons and nature study.

The School Journey Association was set up in 1911 to promote the ideas of J.H. Cowham who advocated fieldwork as a means of bringing geography and science teaching together.

The Kindred of the Kibbo Kift (1920–1935) was a camping, hiking and handicraft group for people of all ages. It had a focus on world peace. It grew out of the Scouting movement, and a breakaway group gave rise to the **Woodcraft Folk** movement in 1924. "Woodcraft" means the skills of living in the open air, close to nature, not making things out of wood.

The Council for the Preservation of Rural England was formed in 1926, and was the first environmental pressure group to demand national education to protect the countryside.

The England and Wales Youth Hostels Association was set up in 1930 to provide inexpensive accommodation and was a measure of the growing use of the countryside for recreation.

The 1930 Housing Act led to widespread slum clearance affecting 15% of the population.

The Mass Trespass of Kinder Scout in 1932 was an act of civil disobedience against the closing off of vast areas of upland England by landowners. In time, it led to a number of important changes about providing access to hills and mountains.

Actuality in the School was a 1938 book that influenced primary schools to bring non-teachers into the classroom, and to use the local environment in their teaching.

1940–1960

The first **Outward Bound** school was opened in the UK in 1941. **The Outward Bound Trust** was set up as an educational charity in 1946 to operate the schools. Gradually, the Outward Bound philosophy evolved from character-training to personal growth and self-discovery. There are now schools in 33 countries.

The Council for the Promotion of Field Studies was formed in 1943 to provide residential centres for school groups so that they could experience scientific fieldwork in the countryside. This major innovation proved a stimulus for greater activity and involvement.

The Nature Conservancy started in 1949 and a key point it made was to stress the need for an educational policy to protect the countryside.

The National Parks and Access to the Countryside Act was passed in 1949.

The Civic Trust was founded in 1957. It campaigned to make better places for people to live. The Civic Trust Awards began in 1959 and continue today.

The Council of Nature was formed in 1958 and, through developments such as National Nature Week, highlighted problems faced by nature.

The Schools and Countryside Report (1958) and **The Study Group on Education and Field Biology** (1963) contributed to the growing interest in schools in nature studies and other countryside focus activities.

1960–2006

The National Rural Studies Association was formed in 1960 to promote rural studies and natural history in schools.

The Observer Wildlife Exhibition illustrated the lack of leadership in relation to promoting effective policy about conservation. This led (in 1963) to a series of study conferences (**The Countryside in 1970**) that were designed to encourage conservation and countryside amenity organisations to work together.

The 1965 Keele conference focused on education with a conscious use of the term environmental education. The recommendation was that this ought to become an essential part of education programmes to ensure that everyone had an understanding of the environment and to promote a scientifically literate society.

The Woodcraft Folk was established as a national charity in 1965.

The Plowden Report in 1967 re-confirmed the value of the environment in the education of young children.

Degree courses in **Environmental Studies** and **Environmental Science** began in the late 1960s.

The Council for Environmental Education began in 1968. Emerging out of the Keele conference, this brought the education and environmental sectors into one body.

The Society of Environmental Education was a teachers' organisation formed in 1968 to encourage the use of the environment in education, and education for the environment.

The 1969 Reith Lecture given by Frank Fraser Darling focused on Wilderness and Plenty and is given the credit for moving "the environment" into the public discourse.

The Skeffington Report *People and Planning* was published in 1969. It proposed that ordinary people be engaged in planning decision-making rather than simply voting for representatives to make decisions on their behalf. That principle continues.

The Department of the Environment was set up in 1970 so that for the first time environmental issues can be considered by one ministry.

The Schools Council Project Environment began in 1970 and explored the relevance of rural studies to environmental education.

The National Association for Outdoor Education was set up in 1970.

School examination syllabuses at age 16 and 18 were created through the 1970s to give students the opportunity to study environmental issues. Teacher education programmes were also set up.

The Ecologist **magazine** was launched in 1970. Its Spring 1971 edition put forward a socially radical Blueprint for Survival. At this time, the term *eco* came into popular usage.

The Town and Country Planning Act was passed in 1971 as a result of the 1969 Skeffington Report.

The National Association for Environmental Education emerged from the National Rural Studies Association in 1971. It, and its journal *Environmental Education*, still exist.

The Town and Country Planning Association Education Unit was set up in 1973, and its *Bulletin of Environmental Education* (BEE) promoted urban environmental studies programmes. **Colin Ward** was its founder-editor.

The Council for Urban Studies Centres was formed in 1974 to encourage the setting up of field studies centres in urban areas.

The National Association for Urban Studies was formed in 1972 with the aim of promoting urban studies and facilitating participation in planning decisions. It promoted green urban areas as healthy places to live.

The Tbilisi intergovernmental conference resulted in the 1977 Tbilisi Declaration which proved a strong influence on international environmental education. The UK government's input to the conference painted a positive picture of what the UK was doing.

Colin Ward publishes *The Child in the City* in 1979. This explores the myriad ways in which children explore the urban landscape. This was a sequel to *Streetwork: The Exploding School* by Fyson and Ward.

Her Majesty's Inspectorate published *Curriculum 11–16: supplementary working papers* in 1979. This said that environmental education "is to be regarded as a function of the whole curriculum, formal and informal … furthered through established subjects and by courses in environmental science and environmental studies which in varying degree are interdisciplinary".[7]

Environmental education was designated as a non-statutory cross-curricular theme in 1990 within the new national curriculum for schools that had been set up in 1988. *Curriculum Guidance 7* on environmental education was published by the National Curriculum Council. All this was welcomed by environmental educators but was a tacit recognition that the national curriculum itself did not mandate a consideration of environmental issues.

A joint **Department for Education/Department for the Environment** conference was held in 1995, and a Government Strategy for Environmental Education was published in 1996.

The **Education for Sustainable Development Panel** was set up by government and issued its first report (*Education for Sustainable Development in the Schools Sector*): a report to the Department for Education and Employment/Qualifications and Curriculum Authority in 1998.[8]

Government launched its **Sustainable Schools Initiative** in 2006 which "places the child at the centre of its concerns for a healthy, just and sustainable society". This was not mandatory and did not include a focus on biodiversity.[9]

The story continues, but the ensuing years have seen a steady decline in the significance of environmental education in schools – just as the problems we face have grown more apparent.

A positive development in recent years has been activity by young people through the climate strikes and their demands that governments take their futures seriously by addressing both the climate and ecological crises that we face. Inspired by Greta Thunberg, the UK Student Climate Network, working through *Teach the Future*, is intent on doing what adult environmental educators have so far failed to do.

Notes

1 Every jurisdiction with a history of environmental learning has a timeline which shows the significant developments. What these don't show are other-country influences on developments.
2 Personal communication 2020.
3 For example, Jones (1803).
4 See Marsden (1997).
5 As we write, however, efforts are still having to be made to de-toxify the air in cities largely because of the growth of vehicle use.
6 Reported in Jenkins and Swinnerton (1996).
7 See: blogs.bath.ac.uk/edswahs/2012/05/28/a-view-from-1979–33-years-on
8 Archived at: tinyurl.com/y7zey9uz
9 Archived at: tinyurl.com/yd3yurtq

Further reading

Clap, B.W. (1994). *An Environmental History of Britain since the Industrial Revolution*. Harlow: Longman.
Fyson, A. & Ward, C. (1973). *Streetwork: The Exploding School*. London: Routledge & Kegan Paul.
Jenkins, E.W. & Swinnerton, B.J. (1996). The School Nature Study Union 1903-94. *History of Education*, 25 (2), 181–198.
Jones, W. (1803). *The Book of Nature; or the True Sense of Things Explained and Made Easy to the Capacities of Children*. London: F&C Rimington.
Marsden, W.E. (1997). Environmental Education: Historical roots, comparative perspectives and current issues in Britain and the United States. *Journal of Curriculum and Supervision*, 13 (1), 92–113.

Martin, G.C. & Wheeler, K. (1975). *Insights into Environmental Education*. Edinburgh: Oliver & Boyd.

Ward, C. (1979). *The Child in the City*. London: Pantheon.

Wheeler, K. (1975). The genesis of environmental education. In G.C. Martin & K. Wheeler (Eds.), *Insights into Environmental Education*. Edinburgh: Oliver & Boyd.

APPENDIX 2

A brief history of environment and learning in the USA

Whilst it is not the case that all interest in the links between learning and nature began in the USA, it is true that without the work of a number of influential North American writers and thinkers, our philosophical and practical understanding of the crucial importance of nature for human survival and fulfilment would either be much poorer or would have developed more slowly. It is woefully ironic, therefore, that 150 years on, the American people could elect leaders who champion the unfettered exploitation of the natural world and who are wilfully blind to the problems this causes.[1]

Influence, however, travels both ways, and it is also the case that many writers and thinkers in North America owed an intellectual debt of gratitude to the 19th-century Prussian polymath Alexander von Humboldt, whom we write about elsewhere. John Muir, for example, wrote to Jeanne Carr, the Wisconsin botanist, "How intensely I desire to be a Humboldt".[2] But then, von Humboldt influenced everyone.

Disinger (1985) argues that there were three precursors to environmental education in the United States: nature study, conservation education, and outdoor education. Carter and Simmons (2010) trace the development of concerns about humanity's effect on nature in the US starting with the mid-19th-century writings of Emerson, Thoreau and Marsh, whom they describe as political and social commentators. This continued in the early to mid-20th century through the output of naturalists such as Muir and then Leopold. The focus of such concerns were mostly resource conservation and habitat preservation rather than anything to do with environment as we understand it today. Whilst some, such as Jackson Turner, saw the changes humans made to the natural world as progress, Muir questioned whether humans should change nature, and Leopold asked how we should change it, given that we inevitably must.[3] Conservation education grew in influence through the century and in the late 1940s outdoor education combined nature study and conservation education to become a common aspect of the school experience. A focus on the state of the environment emerged after World War II and evolved into the modern environmental movement in the 1960s with the early international conferences (IUCN Paris in 1948 and in Nevada in 1970; Stockholm in 1972) being influential in this development. This has continued through the support of educational and not-for-profit organisations (both national and at state level) despite the ebb and flow of federal government interest or hostility, and policy support or negation.

Native Americans (Neolithic to now) lived in greater harmony with the natural world than we do, even as they changed it to fit their needs. Such indigenous worldviews are strong modern influences on the way many think about how we should try to live in the world. Their absence from the story that follows is telling.[4]

The 1800s

Louis Agassiz was a scientist who encouraged his students to learn directly from nature rather than from books.

John James Audubon is probably best known for *Birds of America*, but it was his descriptive essays published in *Delineations of American Scenery and Character*, which first alerted the public to the destruction of the forests.

William Cullen Bryant published *The Prairies* in 1833 whose poems chart the vastness and solitude of the Great Plains beyond the Mississippi.

James Fenimore Cooper portrayed the natural environment in his novels as an obstacle to be dominated and tamed. He saw wilderness as a moral influence, a source of beauty, and a place of adventure.

Ralph Waldo Emerson published his essay *Nature* in 1836 setting out the relationships between humanity and nature, laying the foundations for transcendentalism.[5]

David Henry Thoreau wrote *Walden; or, a life in the woods* in 1854, in which he details two years living in a cabin near Walden Pond. Hirsch[6] says that *Walden* is "a … reference point for green writing and reading, green thinking".[7]

Eunice Foote discovers in 1856 that gases in the atmosphere were affected by the Sun's radiation in different ways, and of all the gases she tested, it was CO_2 that trapped the most heat.[8]

George Perkin Marsh was a politician who, in 1864, wrote *Man and Nature* which carried an early warning about deforestation and desertification. Marsh provided the intellectual link between transcendentalism and conservation.

John Muir popularised spending time in the wild areas as a source of recreation, enjoyment, solace and fulfilment. He was a preservationist whose writing about his travels and about wildlife were read by millions.[9]

The Yosemite Act of 1864 reserved the Yosemite Valley from settlement and gave its care to the state of California as a State Park, and the first National Park (Yellowstone) was established by Congress in 1872. Yosemite became a National Park in 1890.

Carl Schurtz was Secretary of the Interior from 1877 to 1881, when he prosecuted land thieves and promoted public attention of the need for forest preservation.

Teddy Roosevelt, who later became President, founded the Boone and Crockett Club in the mid-1880s, America's first conservation organisation. He worked for the preservation of forest regions before they died out "before the march of settlement".

Wilbur Jackman writes *Nature Study for the Common School* in 1891 which defines the Nature Study movement.

In 1896, the **College of Agriculture** at Cornell University established nature study in rural schools, and in 1899 began its Summer Nature Study School.

Camp Fire Clubs and the **Scouting** movement emerged in the late 1800s/early 1900s; each had exploration and study of the outdoors as key components.

1900 to World War II

The Lacy Act was passed in 1900 and was significant in protecting many species of birds, and **The National Audubon Society** was formed in 1905.

The American Nature Study Society is established in 1908 with **Liberty Hyde Bailey** as its first president. Subsequent presidents include **Anna Botsford Comstock** who published the *Handbook of Nature Study* in 1911.

Enos Mills was encouraged to write by John Muir and founded the first nature guide school. He became the prime motivator for creating Rocky Mountain National Park. He wrote 20 books including *Adventures of a Nature Guide*.

In 1916, **President Wilson** and Congress created the National Park Service within the US Department of Interior to protect the 35 national parks and monuments in existence and those yet to be established.

The Migratory Bird Treaty Act was passed in 1918 which made it illegal to harm most native birds not hunted for sport.

John Dewey published *Experience and Nature* in 1929. The movement for progressive education, led by Dewey, promotes a holistic, student-centred approach that includes learning by doing, integrated and interdisciplinary approaches.

The National Education Association assumed a leadership role in 1935 for conservation education in the schools.

The Education Policies Commission of the **National Education Association** adopted a statement in support of conservation education schools across the US in 1935.

The **Soil Conservation Service** was formed in 1935 leading to the development of conservation education. In the same year Wisconsin was the first state to require teachers to have adequate preparation in the conservation of natural resources.

Post-World War II

The University of Wisconsin – Stevens Point offers a degree in conservation education in 1946.

Robert Steele Funderburk, of Vanderbilt University, writes *The History of Conservation Education in the United States* (1948).

Aldo Leopold writes *A Sand County Almanac* which is published in 1949. Carter and Simmons (2010) describe this as "the cornerstone of the American environmental movement and of modern environmental thinking and writing", adding that Leopold challenged the pursuit of affluence for its own sake.

The **Outdoor Education Association** (OEA) was founded in 1951 and the American Association for Health, Physical Education, and Recreation established the Outdoor Education Project.

The Conservation Education Association is formed in 1953, and in 1954, the **Association of Interpretative Naturalists** (now the National Association for Interpretation).

Vance Packard published *The Waste Makers* in 1960, attacking the economic and environmental costs of careless industrial development.

Rachel Carson published *Silent Spring* in 1962 to acclaim by the conservation movement and condemnation by the chemical industry. Carson warned about the over-use of insecticides in agriculture and its effects on wildlife, which led to a nationwide ban on DDT and other pesticides and to the creation of the US Environmental Protection Agency (EPA).

Steward Udall, the Secretary of State for the Interior, published *The Quiet Crisis* in 1963, highlighting a significant number of existing and imminent environmental problems.

The **Wilderness Act** (1964), the **Species Conservation Act** (1966), the **Wild and Scenic River Act** (1968), the **Solid Waste Disposal Act** (1965) and the **Clean Air Act** (1965) reflected national concerns over the environmental costs of post-war affluence.

The National Wildlife Federation published in 1967 the first volume of *Ranger Rick's Nature Magazine*. This is still being published.

Garrett Hardin published *The Tragedy of the Commons* [10] in 1968, arguing for a management of shared resources to prevent its users over-using it by acting rationally in their own interests.[11]

The first edition of the *Journal of Environmental Education* (**JEE**) is first published in 1969 (initially as *Environmental Education*).

Bill Stapp (with colleagues and students) published *The Concept of Environmental Education* in the first issue of JEE (1969). Stapp served as the first Director of UNESCO's Environmental Education Section (1974–1976).

The **National Environmental Policy Act** is signed by President Nixon on January 1, 1970. In the same year, the **Clean Air Act** was agreed, as was the **National Environmental Education Act** which established an Advisory Council on Environmental Education.

Earth Day is launched in 1970. This began as a teach-in to raise public awareness on critical environmental issues. It still exists.

The National (later North American) Association for Environmental Education (NAAEE) is founded in 1971 as a professional association for environmental educators of all kinds.

Project Learning Tree is launched in 1976 by a consortium of environmental and other organisations. **Project Wild** and **Project Wet** follow, as does WWF's **Windows on the Wild**.

Gary Harvey writes *A Conceptualization of Environmental Education* in 1976 in the report on the North American Regional Seminar on Environmental Education.

John Hug published *Two Hats* in 1977, setting out the liberal education case for enabling students of environmental education to come to their own understanding and conclusions about issues.

JEE published *Goals for Curriculum Development in Environmental Education* (Hungerford, Peyton & Wilke) in 1980.

The **Reagan–Bush years** (1980–1984) were tough for those wanting to protect the natural world and teach about its problems as the US government was not sympathetic to either of these.[12]

The National Environmental Education Act is published in 1990. This sets up an office for environmental education in the EPA, environmental education grants, and training programmes and other initiatives.

The Office of Environmental Justice is established by the EPA in 1992. This followed the First National People of Color Environmental Leadership Summit in 1991.

NAAEE sets out guidelines in 1993 for (i) the development and evaluation of environmental educational materials, and (ii) benchmarks for teacher and student knowledge on environmental topics.

William Cronon published his 1995 essay, "The Trouble with Wilderness", in the *New York Times* arguing that in concentrating on wilderness preservation the environmental movement had failed to value, and protect, the natural world of our everyday lives.[13]

President Bill Clinton issues Executive Order 12898 in 1994, "Federal Actions to Address Environmental Justice in Minority and Low-Income Populations".

The George C. Marshall Institute through its Independent Commission on Environmental Education (now the Environmental Literacy Council) produced *Are We Building Environmental Literacy?* in 1996.

The National Environmental Education Advancement Project holds its first Leadership Clinic in 1996.

Closing the Achievement Gap (using the environment as an integrating context for learning) is published in 1998 by the State Education and Environment Roundtable. This makes the case for the benefits of environmental learning.

NAAEE and the **Environmental Literacy Council** publish *Environmental Studies in the K-12 Classroom: A Teacher's View* in 2000, and the University of Wisconsin – Stevens Point offers the first Fundamentals of Environmental Education online course.

NAAEE published *Excellence in Environmental Education: Guidelines for Learning (K-12)* in 2004.

Last Child in the Woods: Saving our Children from Nature-Deficit Disorder, written by **Richard Louv**, is published in 2005.

The story continues. A recent NAAEE/EPA initiative, jointly with Taiwanese authorities, was to launch the Global Environmental Education Partnership (**GEEP**),[14] which aims to strengthen environmental education practice.

Notes

1 As we write this in early 2020, a Green New Deal has been proposed by US politicians which places the climate near the centre of politics. As *The Economist* notes, however, there are questions about cost-effectiveness. See: tinyurl.com/yyamu5dg
2 Quoted in Wulf (2015).
3 From Richard White's "Biography of William Cronon" in the 2013 American Historical Association Annual Meeting Booklet: tinyurl.com/ydhru8ld
4 A well-known speech about ecological responsibility attributed to Chief Seattle (of the Duwamish Tribe) is of doubtful provenance because of problems of translation and rewriting. Some even doubt that he ever made it. See: tinyurl.com/ycp4y787
5 Emerson wrote: "This invasion of Nature by Trade, with its Money, its Credit, its Steam, its Railroad, threatens to upset the balance of man, and establish a new, universal Monarchy more tyrannical than Babylon or Rome."
6 Nature Poetry: from a poet's glossary: tinyurl.com/y72s5s2o
7 Thoreau's view of the appropriate relationship between humans and the natural world was succinctly stated in his Harvard University commencement address in 1837: "This curious world which we inhabit is more wonderful than it is convenient; more beautiful than it is useful; it is more to be admired than used."
8 See Foote (1856:382).
9 Muir's direct activism helped to save the Yosemite Valley and other areas. His vision of nature's value for its own sake and for its spiritual benefits to humanity helped to change the way we look at the natural world.
10 See the Farnam Street blog: fs.blog/2011/08/the-tragedy-of-the-commons
11 He was a controversial figure because of his anti-immigration and pro-human sterilisation views.
12 Eventually, environmental education itself came under attack for perceived bias.
13 A fuller version of the essay later appeared in Cronon (1995). See also: "The Trouble with Wilderness, or, Getting Back to the Wrong Nature." *Environmental History*, 1 (1) (January 1996), 7–55.
14 The goal of GEEP is to strengthen environmental education around the world by building capacity and focusing on collaboration, sharing best practices, and networking opportunities. See: naaee.org/our-partners/international/geep

Further reading

Carter, R.L. & Simmons, B. (2010). The History and Philosophy of Environmental Education. In A.M. Bodzin, B. Shiner Klein & S. Weaver (Eds.), *The Inclusion of Environmental Education in Science Teacher Education*. Dordrecht: Springer.

Cronon, W. (1995). *Uncommon Ground: Toward Reinventing Nature*. New York, NY: W.W. Norton.

Disinger, J.F. (1983/1997). Environmental Education's Definitional Problem. *ERIC Clearinghouse for Science, Mathematics and Environmental Education Information Bulletin*, 2. Web link: tinyurl.com/yybls7pc

Disinger, J.F. (1985). What research says: Environmental education's definitional problem. *School Science and Mathematics*, 85 (1), 59–68.

Foote, E. (1856). Circumstances affecting the Heat of the Sun's Rays. *American Journal of Science and Arts*, 22 (66).

Hammerman, D. & Hammerman, W. (1973). *Outdoor education: A book of readings*. 2nd edition. Minneapolis, MN: Burgess Publishing Company.

McCrea, E.J. (2006). *The Roots of Environmental Education: How the Past Supports the Future*. Washington, DC: Environmental Education and Training Partnership. Web link: files. eric.ed.gov/fulltext/ED491084.pdf

Marsden, W.E. (1997). Environmental Education: Historical roots, comparative perspectives and current issues in Britain and the United States. *Journal of Curriculum and Supervision*, 13 (1), 92–113.

NAAEE eePRO. (n.d.). *Timeline of EE History*. Washington, DC: North American Association for Environmental Education. Web link: naaee.org/eepro/learning/eelearn/history-ee/lesson-2

Sharp, L.B. & Partridge, E. (Eds.). (1947). Camping and outdoor education. *The Bulletin of the National Association of Secondary-School Principals*, 31 (147).

Stapp, W. (1974). Historical setting of environmental education. In J. Swan and W. Stapp (Eds.), *Environmental Education* (42–49). New York: J. Wiley and Sons.

Swan, M. (1975/1984). Forerunners of environmental education. In N. McInnis and D. Albrecht (Eds.), *What Makes Education Environmental?* (4–20). Medford, NJ: Plexus Pub. Co.

Wulf, A. (2015). *The Invention of Nature the adventures of Alexander von Humboldt*. London: John Murray.

APPENDIX 3

A brief history of environment and learning in Germany

Pre-1800

The first appearance of the term Nachhaltigkeit (sustainability in German) and its first definition go back to the early 18th century. The book *Sylvicultura Oeconomica or: a treatise on husbandry and instructions on the natural growing of wild trees*, was written by the mining administrator **Carl von Carlowitz** in Saxony in 1713, and is generally cited as the first use of the term; this was in the context of forestry.

Carlowitz advocated a "continuous, constant and sustainable use" of the forest. Sustainable forestry, he suggested, was based on the principle that in any given year, only so much timber should be felled as allows a constant supply of mature trees to be ready for felling, thus ensuring that the forest survives and can be managed well.

The 1800s

William von Humboldt (1767–1835) advocated Selbstbildung (self-education) by means of free and active confrontation with, and involvement in, the world. Its objectives were the promotion of individuality, autonomy and universality.

The **Wandervögel** (wandering bird) youth movement started around 1800 in Berlin, inspired by Romanticism, and criticism of ongoing industrialisation. Its objective was to live freely in nature, and develop your own lifestyle.

Alexander von Humboldt (1769–1859) publishes the first volume of *Cosmos* in 1845 with its hundred-page introduction setting out his vision of nature as a "wonderful web of organic life". A second volume appeared in 1847 which explored the internal world of imagination and feelings. *Cosmos* awakened American writers and thinkers to the significance of von Humboldt's ideas, and shaped two generations of American scientists, artists, writers and poets.

Ernst Haeckel (1834–1919) was a zoologist who was greatly influenced by *Cosmos*. He named thousands of new species and coined the word ecology.

Hermann Lietz (1868–1919) founded Landerziehungsheime für Jungen (country boarding schools) inspired by the progressive pedagogy that he observed while working at the Abbotsholme boarding school in Derbyshire, England.

Blut und Boden (Blood and Soil) was a late 19th-century social movement in Germany which celebrated the relationship of a people to the land they lived on and cultivated. It stressed the virtues of rural life and was influenced by the **Völkisch movement** which had its origins in German Romantic Nationalism,[1] which was deeply connected to German culture, history, folklore, and paganism.

The early 20th century

The roots of the environmental movement can be seen in the German youth and reform movement at the beginning of the 20th century and in the reform pedagogy of the 1920s and 1930s.

The **Wandervögel movement** was forcibly integrated into the **Hitlerjugend** (Hitler Youth) in the 1930s.

Richard Walther Darré, Nazi Food and Agriculture Minister, promoted and popularised blood and soil ideology to urge a return to an agrarian economy and a shift away from economic dependence on industry and business.

The 1970s onwards

Since the 1970s, a new environmental (Green) movement has developed, which has now also gained popularity due to criticism of nuclear power and recurrent scandals of environmental pollution, for example by the chemical industry and transport.

The development of different concepts of environmental education in the 1980s included Umwelterziehung (environmental training), Ökologisches Lernen (ecological learning) and Ökopädagogik (ecopedagogy).

Environmental education was initially closely linked to the inclusion of environmental protection issues in school curricula. A corresponding framework was set by the Conference of German Education Ministers in 1980, with its recommendation on environment and education.

The purpose of environmental education was to clarify values and attitudes towards the relationships between people, culture and the natural environment. Experiencing nature and raising awareness of the vulnerability of ecological systems, it was thought, should lead to environmentally compatible behaviour on the part of the individual within the framework of interdisciplinary and action–oriented learning processes. The framework was provided by an interdisciplinary approach that focused on biology, geography and social studies.

Wolfgang Klafki (1992) related education to Epochal Typische Schlüsselprobleme (Epochal Typical Key Problems): These he saw as:

1. the question of war and peace
2. environmental questions/the ecological questions
3. the rapid growth of the world population
4. socially produced inequality
5. the threats and opportunities of the new technical control, information and communication media
6. the subjectiveness of the individual and the phenomenon of the me-you relationship against the background of the tension between individual aspirations for happiness, interpersonal responsibility and the recognition of the other[2]

The 1990s also saw the legitimisation of sustainable development as a political objective, the politicisation of education, and pedagogical work on the political objective of sustainable development.

Germany's first official education policy statement on ESD was provided in 1998 by *BLK Booklet 69 Education for Sustainable Development – an Orientation Framework*.

Gerhard de Haan and **Dorothee Harenberg** (1999) pointed out the importance of certain competences for enabling learners to contribute to sustainable development. They created the concept of Gestaltungskompetenz (shaping competence).

Launched in 1999 with a duration of five years, the 21 programme had a significant impact on the implementation of ESD in schools and developed didactic concepts around ESD.

The 2000s

The early 2000s saw the structural embedding of ESD into educational processes. For example, ESD had its own working group within the German Association for Educational Research. This later merged with the intercultural education group to form a new section: Upgrading.

The year 2004 saw the launch of the programme Transfer-21 which had an impact on the implementation of ESD in schools and developed didactic concepts on ESD. Many activities in the context of the UN Decade of ESD were developed.

In 2017 a national action plan for ESD was developed as part of the UNESCO Global Action Programme initiative. Recent research topics included quality assessment, sustainable development as a topic of education, the development of a recognised ESD approach, and competence measurement.

Notes

1 And to efforts to create Germany as a single country.
2 This is available at: tinyurl.com/t87pcqj

APPENDIX 4

The 17 Sustainable Development Goals

2015 saw the Paris Agreement on climate change and the launch of the Sustainable Development Goals (SDGs) whose purpose is to transform people's lives. The 17 goals (and 169 targets) cover our most pressing contemporary issues: poverty, hunger, equality, energy, clean water and sanitation, biodiversity, climate change, economic growth, sustainable cities, and responsible consumption, as well as strategies such as education and justice. The goals are:

1. **No poverty.** End poverty in all its forms everywhere.
2. **Zero hunger.** End hunger, achieve food security and improved nutrition, and promote sustainable agriculture.
3. **Good health and well-being for people.** Ensure healthy lives and promote well-being for all at all ages.
4. **Quality education.** Ensure inclusive and equitable quality education and promote lifelong learning opportunities for all.
5. **Gender equality.** Achieve gender equality and empower all women and girls.
6. **Clean water and sanitation.** Ensure availability and sustainable management of water and sanitation for all.
7. **Affordable and clean energy.** Ensure access to affordable, reliable, sustainable and modern energy for all.
8. **Decent work and economic growth.** Promote sustained, inclusive and sustainable economic growth, full and productive employment, and decent work for all.
9. **Industry, innovation and infrastructure.** Build resilient infrastructure, promote inclusive and sustainable industrialisation, and foster innovation.
10. **Reducing inequalities.** Reduce income inequality within and among countries.

11. **Sustainable cities and communities.** Make cities and human settlements inclusive, safe, resilient and sustainable.
12. **Responsible consumption and production.** Ensure sustainable consumption and production patterns.
13. **Climate action.** Take urgent action to combat climate change and its impacts by regulating emissions and promoting developments in renewable energy.
14. **Life below water.** Conserve and sustainably use the oceans, seas and marine resources for sustainable development.
15. **Life on land.** Protect, restore and promote sustainable use of terrestrial ecosystems, sustainably manage forests, combat desertification, halt and reverse land degradation, and halt biodiversity loss.
16. **Peace, justice and strong institutions.** Promote peaceful and inclusive societies for sustainable development, provide access to justice for all, and build effective, accountable and inclusive institutions at all levels.
17. **Partnerships for the goals.** Strengthen the means of implementation and revitalise the global partnership for sustainable development.

INDEX

Printed in Great Britain
by Amazon